Glencoe
CHEMISTRY
MATTER AND CHANGE

ChemLab and MiniLab Worksheets

 Glencoe
McGraw-Hill

New York, New York   Columbus, Ohio   Woodland Hills, California   Peoria, Illinois

A GLENCOE PROGRAM

Glencoe
CHEMISTRY
MATTER AND CHANGE

Hands-On Learning:
Laboratory Manual, SE/TE
Forensics Laboratory Manual, SE/TE
CBL Laboratory Manual, SE/TE
Small-Scale Laboratory Manual, SE/TE
ChemLab and MiniLab Worksheets

Review/Reinforcement:
Study Guide for Content Mastery, SE/TE
Solving Problems: A Chemistry Handbook
Reviewing Chemistry
Guided Reading Audio Program

Applications and Enrichment:
Challenge Problems
Supplemental Problems

Assessment:
Chapter Assessment
MindJogger Videoquizzes (VHS)
TestCheck Software, Windows/Macintosh

Teacher Resources:
Lesson Plans
Block Scheduling Lesson Plans
Spanish Resources
Section Focus Transparencies and Masters
Math Skills Transparencies and Masters
Teaching Transparencies and Masters
Solutions Manual

Technology:
Chemistry Interactive CD-ROM
Vocabulary PuzzleMaker Software,
    Windows/Macintosh
Glencoe Science Web site:
science.glencoe.com

Send all inquiries to:
Glencoe/McGraw-Hill
8787 Orion Place
Columbus, OH 43240-4027

ISBN 0-07-824534-6
Printed in the United States of America.
5 6 7 8 9 10 045 09 08 07 06

Contents

To the Teacher

ChemLab and MiniLab Worksheets includes masters of all the ChemLabs and MiniLabs found in **Chemistry: Matter and Change**. These are expanded versions that allow students to complete the activity in most cases without having to take their textbooks into the laboratory. Data tables are enlarged so that students can record actual data. Lab questions are reprinted with lines on which students can write their answers. In addition, for student safety, all appropriate safety symbols and caution statements have been reproduced on these expanded pages. Reduced answer pages for each ChemLab and MiniLab are provided at the back of the book.

Equipment and Materials List

These easy-to-use tables of materials can help you prepare for your chemistry classes for the year. All quantities are for one lab setup of each *MiniLab* or *ChemLab* for the entire course. Before placing your order for supplies, determine how many classes you will be teaching and how many students you expect in each class. For example, if you have ten groups of students in each of seven classes, multiply the quantities of materials by 70 to arrive at your total course requirements.

The standard list of equipment is made up of a set of equipment that is generally recommended for each lab bench station in the chemistry laboratory. For all lab activities in this program, it is assumed that your classroom is equipped with these items for each setup of a *MiniLab* or *ChemLab*. Additional equipment required for the course is listed under **Nonconsumables.** The listed amounts of **Chemicals** and **Other Consumables** for *MiniLabs* and *ChemLabs* are sufficient for one lab setup per student or group of students.

Standard Equipment List (for each station)

apron, 1 per student	funnel
goggles, 1 pair per student	graduated cylinder, 10-mL
beakers, 100-mL, 2	graduated cylinder, 50-mL or 100-mL
beakers, 250-mL, 2	microplate, 24-well
beakers, 400-mL, 2	microplate, 96-well
beaker tongs	scissors
Bunsen burner and tubing	spatula, stainless steel
clay triangle	stirring rods, 2
crucible and cover	test-tube holder
crucible tongs	test-tube rack
droppers, 2	test tubes, 6 large
Erlenmeyer flask, 125-mL	test tubes, 6 small
Erlenmeyer flask, 250-mL	wash bottle
evaporating dish	watch glass
forceps	wire gauze

Classroom Equipment (for general use)

balance	iron rings, assorted
beakers, assorted small 50-mL, 150-mL	iron tripod
beakers, assorted large 600-mL, 800-mL, 1-L, 2-L	lighter for burner
CBL system, including sensors and cables	mortar and pestle
ChemBio software	ring stands, 2
clamps, assorted including burette clamps	rubber or Tygon tubing
conductivity tester	rubber stoppers, assorted
dishpan, plastic	thermometer, −10°C to 150°C
Erlenmeyer flasks, 500-mL, 1-L	thermometer clamp
hot plate	

Equipment and Materials List, *continued*

These easy-to-use tables of equipment and consumable materials can help you prepare for your chemistry classes for the year. Quantities listed for *ChemLabs* and *MiniLabs* are the maximum quantities you will need for one student group for the year. The Student Edition pages on which each item is used are listed in parentheses after the quantities. Refer to the *Resource Manager* in front of each chapter in the Teacher Wraparound Edition for a list of equipment and materials used for each laboratory activity in the chapter.

Non-Consumables

Item	ChemLab	MiniLab
barometer	1 (pp. 444, 728)	1 (p. 438)
basting bulb	1 (p. 796)	
beaker, 50-mL	1 (p. 78)	1 (p. 604)
beaker, 150-mL	1 (p. 374)	4 (pp. 295, 681, 715)
beaker, 600-mL	1 (p. 796)	1 (p. 786)
beaker, 600-mL with graduations	1 (p. 444)	
beaker, 1-L		1 (p. 438)
bucket, 4-L	1 (p. 444)	
burette, 50-mL	1 (p. 626)	
cuvette	1 (p. 480)	
diffraction grating	1 (p. 142)	
dropper	5 (pp. 108, 202, 410, 626)	3 (pp. 573, 848)
flask, 275-mL polystyrene culture	4 (p. 142)	
flask, 500-mL Florence	1 (p. 626)	
funnel, powder		1 (p. 222)
graduated cylinder, 25-mL	1 (p. 202)	1 (pp. 15, 28, 786)
graduated cylinder, 50-mL	1 (pp. 78, 480)	
graduated cylinder, 250-mL	1 (p. 862)	
hair dryer	1 (p. 18)	
hammer	1 (p. 170)	
lightbulb, 40-watt tubular with socket and power cord	1 (p. 142)	
lightbulb, 150-watt with socket and clamp	1 (p. 862)	
mass, 500 g	1 (p. 18)	
meterstick	1 (p. 18)	
pennies, pre- and post-1982		100 (pp. 102, 819)
petri dish with lid	1 (pp. 78, 832)	2 (pp. 15, 751, 848)
pipette, Beral-type	5 (pp. 688, 766)	1 (p. 751)
pipette, thin-stem	3 (p. 586)	
pipette	4 (pp. 300, 480, 796)	
pipette filler (bulb)	1 (pp. 480, 550)	
pipette, dropping	1 (p. 654)	1 (p. 604)

Equipment and Materials List, continued

Non-Consumables, continued

Item	ChemLab	MiniLab
pipette, graduated	1 (p. 550)	
pipette, plastic microtip	1 (p. 444)	
pneumatic trough	1 (p. 728)	
power supply, spectrum tube	2 (p. 142)	
rubber stopper assembly, #5	1 (p. 796)	
ruler	1 (pp. 46, 202, 268, 550)	1 (pp. 438, 715)
spectrum tubes (hydrogen and neon)	1 ea. (p. 142)	
spoon		1 (p. 638)
stopwatch (timer, clock)	1 (pp. 410, 550, 766)	1 (pp. 329, 539, 848)
test tube, large	3 (p. 202)	
test tube, small	6 (pp. 170, 410, 480, 550, 796)	2 (pp. 184, 573, 751)
towel, cloth	1 (p. 766)	
tubing, glass	20 cm (p. 444)	
washer, metal		1 (p. 28)
weighing bottle	1 (p. 626)	
wire cutters	1 (p. 300)	
wire screen		10 cm × 10 cm (p. 329)
CBL DIN adapter and cable	1 (pp. 480, 796)	
CBL link cable	1 (pp. 796, 832, 862)	
CBL-P adapter	1 (p. 832)	
CBL temperature probe	2 (p. 862)	
CBL Vernier colorimeter	1 (p. 480)	
CBL Vernier pressure sensor	1 (p. 796)	
CBL voltage probe	1 (p. 688)	
RADIATIN software program	1 (p. 832)	
student radiation monitor	1 (p. 832)	
TI GRAPH LINK and cable	1 (pp. 480, 832, 862)	

Chemicals

Item	ChemLab	MiniLab
2-propanol, 91% (isopropanol)	1 mL (p. 410)	
2-propanol, 95% (isopropanol)	2 mL (p. 766)	
acetic acid, glacial		12 mL (pp. 438, 604)
acetone	300 mL (pp. 268, 410)	
aluminum nitrate	6 g (pp. 300, 688)	
aluminum strip	1 (p. 688)	
aluminum wire	10 cm (p. 300)	
bromcresol green indicator		2 mL (p. 848)

Equipment and Materials List, *continued*

Chemicals, continued

Item	ChemLab	MiniLab
calcium carbide		1 g (p. 715)
calcium chloride		0.1 g (p. 125)
cobalt(II) chloride hexahydrate		0.25 g (p. 573)
copper metal	1 g (p. 654)	
copper shot	40 g (p. 46)	
copper strip	1 (p. 688)	10 cm (p. 681)
copper(II) nitrate	28 g (pp. 300, 688)	
copper(II) sulfate pentahydrate	12 g (p. 374)	
ethanol, 95%	3 mL (pp. 410, 766)	12 mL (p. 786)
hydrochloric acid, 12*M*	30 mL (pp. 170, 550)	15 mL (pp. 184, 573)
iron filings (20 mesh)	2 g (p. 374)	
lithium chloride		0.1 g (p.125)
magnesium nitrate	3 g (p. 300, 688)	
magnesium ribbon	42 cm (pp. 232, 550, 688)	13 cm (pp. 184, 681)
magnesium sulfate heptahydrate, (Epsom salts)	6 g (pp. 202, 342	6 g (p. 295)
magnesium sulfate, anhydrous	1 g (p. 202)	
methanol	2 mL (p. 766)	3 mL (p. 751)
nitric acid, 16*M*	38 mL (p. 654)	
phenolphthalein solution	1 mL (p. 626)	1 mL (p. 715)
potassium chloride	10 g (p. 832)	0.1 g (p. 125)
potassium hydrogen phthalate	0.5 g (p. 626)	
potassium nitrate	1 g (p. 688)	
potassium nitrite		0.5 g (p. 848)
rock salt		100 g (p. 473)
salicylic acid		1.5 g (p. 751)
silver nitrate	5.5 g (pp. 78, 586)	
sodium chloride (table salt)	40 g (p. 862)	70 g (pp. 125, 573, 638, 681, 786)
sodium chloride	6 g (p. 586)	
sodium hydrogen carbonate (baking soda)		38 g (pp. 362, 438, 638)
sodium hydroxide	4 g (p. 626)	9 g (pp. 295, 786)
sodium sulfide	0.2 g (p. 586)	
strontium chloride		0.1 g (p. 125)
sucrose (table sugar)	1 g (p. 796)	
sulfuric acid, 18*M*		2 mL (pp. 751, 848)
washing soda	0.2 g (p. 202)	
zinc nitrate	33 g (pp. 300, 688)	
zinc strip	5 (pp. 300, 688)	

Equipment and Materials List, *continued*

Other Consumables

Item	ChemLab	MiniLab
aluminum foil	12 cm × 12 cm (p. 268)	30 cm × 30 cm (p. 438) 5 cm × 5 cm (p. 638)
ammonia, household	11 mL (pp. 410, 654)	
bag, 1-gallon plastic zip-close		1 (p. 848)
balloon, 9-inch latex	2 (p. 108)	
bottle, 1-L plastic soft drink with cap	1 (p. 728)	
bottle, 2-L plastic soft drink with cap	1 (p. 268)	
candle		1 (p. 438)
cardboard	10 cm × 10 cm (p. 766)	2 cm × 2 cm (p. 184)
cheesecloth		20 cm × 20 cm (p. 786)
chewing gum		2 pieces (p. 329)
chromatography paper	3 (p. 268)	
cooking oil	2 mL (p. 796)	1 mL (p. 15)
cotton ball		1 (p. 751)
cup, 5-oz. plastic	1 (p. 46)	1 (p. 819)
cup, 9-oz. plastic		2 (p. 68)
cup, foam		1 (p. 504)
detergent, liquid dish	1 mL (p. 202)	6 mL (pp. 15, 715)
dish, black plastic frozen dinner	1 (p. 862)	
drain cleaner, crystal Drano®	10 g (p. 654)	
duster, aerosol can	1 (p. 444)	
effervescent antacid tablet		1 (p. 539)
filter paper	3 (pp. 78, 202, 688)	2 (p. 68)
food coloring (red, blue, green, yellow)	0.1 mL ea. (p. 142)	1 mL ea. (p. 15)
food coloring, blue	0.5 mL (p. 480)	
gumdrops, small		3 (p. 261)
hairpin		3 (p. 230)
label	4 (p. 550)	
leaf samples from deciduous trees or plants, fresh	3 (p. 268)	
marker, water-soluble black		1 (p. 68)
marshmallows, mini-sized		9 (p. 261)
marshmallows, regular-sized		3 (p. 261)
matches	1 (p. 520)	6 (pp. 184, 438, 715)
milk, whole		50 mL (p. 15)
nail, iron		4 (p. 681)

Other Consumables, *continued*

Item	ChemLab	MiniLab
nail, large iron		1 (p. 68)
paper clip	1 (p. 78)	
paper towel	12 (pp. 410, 728)	3 (p. 329)
paper, graph	1 sheet (p. 46)	2 sheets (pp. 164, 819)
paper, white		1 sheet (p. 848)
pen, marking	1 (p. 410)	
pencil	3 (pp. 46, 268)	
pencil, glass-marking	1 (p. 170)	
pencil, grease	1 (pp. 202, 410)	
pencils, colored, assorted	1 set (p. 142)	
potato chip, large	1 (p. 520)	
rubber band, large	1 (p. 18)	1 (p. 715)
sandpaper, fine (10 cm × 10 cm)	1 (pp. 300, 550)	2 (pp. 184, 681)
silver object, small tarnished		1 (p. 638)
steel wool, pad	1 (p. 688)	1 (p. 638)
straw, plastic soda		12 (p. 401)
swab, cotton	6 (p. 480)	6 (p. 125)
tape, clear plastic	12 cm (p. 268)	
tape, electrical	20 cm (p. 444)	
tape, masking	10 cm (p. 410)	30 cm (p. 438)
tissue, facial	11 (pp. 480, 766)	
toothpick		22 (pp. 15, 261)
twist tie	1 (p. 766)	
vanilla extract	6 mL (p. 108)	
vegetable shortening, solid		25 g (p. 786)
waxed paper	30 cm × 30 cm (p. 410)	
weighing paper	1 (p. 374)	4 (pp. 295, 329, 751)
wire, 12-gauge copper	0.5 m (p. 46)	
wire, 18-gauge copper	0.5 m (p. 46)	
wire, 22- or 26- gauge copper		2 m (p. 401)
wire, copper	18 cm (pp. 78, 300)	
wire, lead	10 cm (p. 300)	
wood splint		4 (pp. 184, 638, 715)
yeast, active dry	1 pkg. (p. 796)	

miniLAB 1
Developing Observation Skills

Observing and Inferring A chemist's ability to make careful and accurate observations is developed early. The observations often are used to make inferences. An inference is an explanation or interpretation of observations.

Materials petri dish (2), graduated cylinder, whole milk, water, vegetable oil, four different food colorings, toothpick (2), dishwashing detergent

Procedure

1. Add water to a petri dish to a height of 0.5 cm. Add 1 mL of vegetable oil.
2. Dip the end of a toothpick in liquid dishwashing detergent.
3. Touch the tip of the toothpick to the water at the center of the petri dish. Record your detailed observations.
4. Add whole milk to a second petri dish to a height of 0.5 cm.
5. Place one drop each of four different food colorings in four different locations on the surface of the milk. Do not put a drop of food coloring in the center.
6. Repeat steps 2 and 3.

Analysis

1. What did you observe in step 3?

_____

_____

_____

2. What did you observe in step 6?

_____

_____

_____

3. Oil, the fat in milk, and grease belong to a class of chemicals called lipids. What can you infer about the addition of detergent to dishwater?

_____

_____

_____

Chemistry: Matter and Change • Chapter 1 **1**

CHEMLAB 1

The Rubber Band Stretch

Galileo Galilei (1564–1642) was an Italian philosopher, astronomer, and mathematician. Galileo pioneered the use of a systematic method of observation, experimentation, and analysis as a way to discover facts about nature. Modern science has its roots in Galileo's 17th-century work on the art of experimentation. This chapter introduced you to how scientists approach their work. In this **CHEMLAB,** you will have a chance to design a scientific method to study something you have observed many times before—the stretching of a rubber band.

Problem

What happens when you heat a stretched rubber band?

Objectives

- **Observe** the properties of a stretched and a relaxed rubber band.
- **Form a hypothesis** about the effect of heat on a stretched rubber band.
- **Design** an experiment to test your hypothesis.
- **Collect** and **analyze** data.
- **Draw conclusions** based on your analysis.

Materials

large rubber band
500-g mass
ring stand
clamp
hair dryer
meterstick or ruler

Safety Precautions

- Frequently observe the rubber band for any splits. Discard if rubber band is defective.
- The hair dryer can become hot, so handle it with care.

Pre-Lab

1. Heat is the transfer of energy from a warmer object to a cooler object. If an object feels warm to your finger, your finger is cooler than the object and energy is being transferred from the object to your finger. In what direction does the energy flow if an object feels cooler to you?

_____

_____

2. Your forehead is very sensitive to hot and cold. How can you use this fact to detect whether an object is giving off or absorbing heat?

_____

_____

_____

_____

3. Read the entire **CHEMLAB.** It is important to know exactly what you are going to do during all chemistry experiments so you can use your laboratory time efficiently and safely. What is the problem that this experiment is going to explore?

_____

_____

4. What typical steps in a scientific method will you use to explore the problem? Write down the procedure that you will use in each experiment that you design. Be sure to include all safety precautions.

Copyright © Glencoe/McGraw-Hill, a division of the McGraw-Hill Companies, Inc.

CHEMLAB 1

5. You will need to record the data that you collect during each experiment. Use the data tables below.

Rubber Band Data	
Experiment #	**Observations**
Trial 1	
Trial 2	
Trial 3	
Trial 4	

Rubber Band Data	
Experiment #	**Observations**
Trial 1	
Trial 2	
Trial 3	
Trial 4	

Rubber Band Data	
Experiment #	**Observations**
Trial 1	
Trial 2	
Trial 3	
Trial 4	

Procedure

1. Obtain one large rubber band. Examine the rubber band for any splits or cracks. If you find any defects, discard it and obtain a new one.

2. Record detailed observations of the unstretched rubber band.

3. Design your first experiment to observe whether heat is given off or absorbed by a rubber band as it is stretched. Have your teacher approve your plan.

4. Do repeated trials of your experiment until you are sure of the results. **CAUTION:** *Do not bring the rubber band near your face unless you are wearing goggles.*

5. Design a second experiment to observe whether heat is given off or absorbed by a rubber band as it contracts after being stretched. Have your teacher approve your plan.

6. Do repeated trials of your experiment until you are sure of the results.

7. Use your observations in steps 2, 4, and 6 to form a hypothesis and make a prediction about what will happen to a stretched rubber band when it is heated.

8. Use the remaining items in the list of materials to design a third experiment to test what happens to a stretched rubber band as it is heated. Have your teacher approve your plan. Be sure to record all observations before, during, and after heating.

Cleanup and Disposal

1. Return the rubber band to your teacher to be reused by other classes.

2. Allow the hair dryer to cool before putting it away.

Analyze and Conclude

1. Observing and Inferring What results did you observe in step 4 of the procedure? Was energy gained or lost by the rubber band? By your forehead? Explain.

_____

_____

CHEMLAB 1

2. Observing and Inferring What results did you observe in step 6 of the procedure? Was energy gained or lost by the rubber band? By your forehead? Explain.

_____

_____

3. Applying Many substances expand when they are heated. Did the rubber band behave in the same way? How do you know?

_____

_____

4. Drawing a Conclusion Did the result of heating the stretched rubber band in step 8 confirm or refute your hypothesis? Explain.

_____

_____

5. Making Predictions What would happen if you applied ice to the stretched rubber band?

_____

6. Error Analysis Compare your results and conclusion with those of your classmates. What were your independent and dependent variables? Did you use a control? Did all of the lab teams measure the same variables? Were the data that you collected qualitative or quantitative? Does this make a difference when reporting your data to others? Do your results agree? Why or why not?

_____

_____

_____

_____

_____

Real-World Chemistry

1. When you put ice in a glass so that the ice rises higher than the rim, water does not over-flow the glass when the ice melts. Explain.

_____

_____

2. Why do you think temperature extremes must be taken into account when bridges and highways are designed?

_____

_____

miniLAB 2

Density of an Irregular Solid

Measuring To calculate density, you need to know both the mass and volume of an object. You can find the volume of an irregular solid by displacing water.

Materials balance, graduated cylinder, water, washer or other small object

Procedure 👐 🥽

1. Find and record the mass of the washer.
2. Add about 15 mL of water to your graduated cylinder. Measure and record the volume. Because the surface of the water in the cylinder is curved, make volume readings at eye level and at the lowest point on the curve. The curved surface is called a *meniscus*.
3. Carefully add the washer to the cylinder. Then measure and record the new volume.

Analysis

1. Use the initial and final volume readings to calculate the volume of the washer.

   _____

2. Use the calculated volume and the measured mass to find the density of the washer.

   _____

3. Explain why you cannot use displacement of water to find the volume of a sugar cube.

   _____

4. The washer is a short cylinder with a hole in the middle. Describe another way to find its volume.

   _____

   _____

   _____

CHEMLAB 2

Using Density to Find the Thickness of a Wire

The thickness of wire often is measured using a system called the American Wire Gauge (AWG) standard. The smaller the gauge number, the larger the diameter of the wire. For example, 18-gauge copper wire has a diameter of about 0.102 cm; 12-gauge copper wire has a diameter of about 0.205 cm. Such small diameters are difficult to measure accurately with a metric ruler. In this experiment, you will plot measurements of mass and volume to find the density of copper. Then, you will use the density of copper to confirm the gauge of copper wire.

Problem

How can density be used to verify the diameter of copper wire?

Objectives

- **Collect** and **graph** mass and volume data to find the density of copper.
- **Measure** the length and volume of a copper wire, and **calculate** its diameter.
- **Calculate** percent errors for the results.

Materials

tap water
100-mL graduated cylinder
small cup, plastic
balance
copper shot
copper wire (12-gauge, 18-gauge)

metric ruler
pencil
graph paper
graphing calculator (optional)

Safety Precautions

- **Always wear safety goggles and a lab apron.**

Pre-Lab

1. Read the entire **CHEMLAB.**

2. What is the equation used to calculate density?

_____

_____

3. How can you find the volume of a solid that has an irregular shape?

_____

_____

_____

4. What is a meniscus and how does it affect volume readings?

_____

_____

_____

5. If you plot mass versus volume, what property of matter will the slope of the graph represent?

_____

_____

6. How do you find the slope of a graph?

_____

_____

_____

7. A piece of copper wire is a narrow cylinder. The equation for the volume of a cylinder is

$$V = \pi r^2 h$$

where V is the volume, r is the radius, h is the height, and π (pi) is a constant with a value of 3.14. Rearrange the equation to solve for r.

_____

CHEMLAB (2)

8. What is the relationship between the diameter and the radius of a cylinder?

_____

_____

9. Use the two data tables below.

Density of Copper			
Trial	Mass of copper added	Total mass of copper	Total volume of water displaced
1			
2			
3			
4			

Diameter of Copper Wire		
	12-gauge	18-gauge
Length		
Mass		
Measured diameter		
Calculated diameter		

Procedure

Record all measurements in the data tables.

1. Pour about 20 mL of water into a 100-mL graduated cylinder. Read the actual volume.

2. Find the mass of the plastic cup.

3. Add about 10 g of copper shot to the cup and find the mass again.

4. Pour the copper shot into the graduated cylinder and read the new volume.

5. Repeat steps 3 and 4 three times. By the end of the four trials, you will have about 40 g of copper in the graduated cylinder.

6. Obtain a piece of 12-gauge copper wire and a piece of 18-gauge copper wire. Use a metric ruler to measure the length and diameter of each wire.

7. Wrap each wire around a pencil to form a coil. Remove the coils from the pencil. Find the mass of each coil.

Cleanup and Disposal

1. Carefully drain off most of the water from the graduated cylinder. Make sure all of the copper shot remains in the cylinder.

2. Pour the copper shot onto a paper towel to dry. Both the copper shot and wire can be reused.

Analyze and Conclude

1. Using Numbers Complete the table for the density of copper by calculating the total mass of copper and the total water displaced for each trial.

_____

2. Making and Using Graphs Graph total mass versus total volume of copper. Draw a line that best fits the points. Then use two points on your line to find the slope of your graph. Because density equals mass divided by volume, the slope will give you the density of copper.

_____

If you are using a graphing calculator, select the 5:FIT CURVE option from the MAIN MENU of the ChemBio program. Choose 1:LINEAR L1,L2 from the REGRESSION/LIST to help you plot and calculate the slope of the graph.

CHEMLAB 2

3. Using Numbers Calculate the percent error for your value of density.

4. Using Numbers To complete the second data table, you must calculate the diameter for each wire. Use the accepted value for the density of copper and the mass of each wire to calculate volume. Then use the equation for the volume of a cylinder to solve for the radius. Double the radius to find the diameter.

_____

5. Comparing and Contrasting How do your calculated values for the diameter compare to your measured values and to the AWG values listed in the introduction?

_____

6. Error Analysis How could you change the procedure to reduce the percent error for density?

_____

_____

Real-World Chemistry

1. There is a standard called the British Imperial Standard Wire Gauge (SWG) that is used in England and Canada. Research the SWG standard to find out how it differs from the AWG standard. Are they the only standards used for wire gauge?

_____

_____

_____

_____

2. Interview an electrician or a building inspector who reviews the wiring in new or re-modeled buildings. Ask what the codes are for the wires used and how the diameter of a wire affects its ability to safely conduct electricity. Ask to see a wiring diagram.

_____

_____

_____

_____

miniLAB 3
Separating Ink Dyes

Applying Concepts Chromatography is an important diagnostic tool for chemists. Many types of substances can be separated and analyzed using this technique. In this experiment, you will use paper chromatography to separate the dyes in water-soluble black ink.

Materials 9-oz wide-mouth plastic cups (2); round filter paper; 1/4 piece of 11-cm round filter paper; scissors; pointed object, approximately 3–4 mm diameter; water-soluble black felt pen or marker

Procedure

1. Fill one of the wide-mouth plastic cups with water to about 2 cm from the top. Wipe off any water drops on the lip of the cup.

2. Place the round filter paper on a clean, dry surface. Make a concentrated ink spot in the center of the paper by firmly pressing the tip of the pen or marker onto the paper.

3. Use a sharp object to create a small hole, approximately 3–4 mm or about the diameter of a pen tip, in the center of the ink spot.

4. Roll the 1/4 piece of filter paper into a tight cone. This will act as a wick to draw the ink. Work the pointed end of the wick into the hole in the center of the round filter paper.

5. Place the paper/wick apparatus on top of the cup of water, with the wick in the water. The water will move up the wick and outward through the round paper.

6. When the water has moved to within about 1 cm of the edge of the paper (about 20 minutes), carefully remove the paper from the water-filled cup and put it on the empty cup.

Analysis

1. Make a drawing of the round filter paper and label the color bands. How many distinct dyes can you identify?

2. Why do you see different colors at different locations on the filter paper?

_____

_____

_____

3. How does your chromatogram compare with those of your classmates who used other types of black felt pens or markers? Explain the differences.

_____

_____

CHEMLAB 3

Matter and Chemical Reactions

One of the most interesting characteristics of matter, and one that drives the study and exploration of chemistry, is the fact that matter changes. By examining a dramatic chemical reaction, such as the reaction of the element copper and the compound silver nitrate in a water solution, you can readily observe chemical change. Drawing on one of the fundamental laboratory techniques introduced in this chapter, you can separate the products. Then, you will use a flame test to confirm the identity of the products.

Problem

Is there evidence of a chemical reaction between copper and silver nitrate? If so, which elements reacted and what is the name of the compound they formed?

Objectives

- **Observe** the reactants as they change into product.
- **Separate** a mixture by filtration.
- **Predict** the names of the products.

Materials

copper wire
$AgNO_3$ solution
sandpaper
stirring rod
50-mL graduated cylinder
50-mL beaker
funnel
filter paper

250-mL Erlenmeyer flask
ring stand
small iron ring
plastic petri dish
paper clip
Bunsen burner
tongs

Safety Precautions

- **Always wear safety goggles, gloves, and a lab apron.**
- **Silver nitrate is toxic and will harm skin and clothing.**
- **Use caution around a flame.**

Pre-Lab

1. Read the entire **CHEMLAB.**

2. Prepare all written materials that you will take into the laboratory. Be sure to include safety precautions and procedure notes. Use the data table on the next page.

3. Define the terms physical property and chemical property. Give an example of each.

_____

_____

_____

_____

_____

4. Form a hypothesis regarding what you might observe if
   a. a chemical change occurs.

   _____

   _____

   _____

   _____

   _____

   b. a physical change occurs.

   _____

   _____

   _____

   _____

   _____

CHEMLAB 3

5. Distinguish between a homogeneous mixture and a heterogeneous mixture.

_____

_____

_____

_____

_____

_____

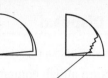

Tear corner

7. Use the ring stand, small iron ring, funnel, Erlenmeyer flask, and filter paper to set up a filtration apparatus. Attach the iron ring to the ring stand. Adjust the height of the ring so the end of the funnel is inside the neck of the Erlenmeyer flask.

8. To fold the filter paper, examine the diagram above. Begin by folding the circle in half, then fold in half again. Tear off the lower right corner of the flap that is facing you. This will help the filter paper stick better to the funnel. Open the folded paper into a cone. Place the filter paper cone in the funnel.

Procedure

1. Obtain 8 cm of copper wire. Rub the copper wire with the sandpaper until it is shiny.

2. Measure approximately 25 mL $AgNO_3$ (silver nitrate) solution into a 50-mL beaker. **CAUTION:** *Do not allow to contact skin or clothing.*

3. Make and record an observation of the physical properties of the copper wire and $AgNO_3$ solution.

4. Coil the piece of copper wire to a length that will fit into the beaker. Make a hook on the end of the coil to allow the coil to be suspended from the stirring rod.

5. Hook the coil onto the middle of the stirring rod. Place the stirring rod across the top of the beaker immersing some of the coil in the $AgNO_3$ solution.

6. Make and record observations of the wire and the solution every five minutes for 20 minutes.

9. Remove the coil from the beaker and dispose of it as directed by your teacher. Some of the solid product may form a mixture with the liquid in the beaker. Decant the liquid by slowly pouring it down the stirring rod into the funnel. Solid product will be caught in the filter paper. Collect the filtrate—the liquid that runs through the filter paper—in the Erlenmeyer flask.

10. Transfer the clear filtrate to a petri dish.

11. Adjust a Bunsen burner flame until it is blue. Hold the paper clip with tongs in the flame until no additional color is observed. **CAUTION:** *The paper clip will be very hot.*

12. Using tongs, dip the hot paper clip in the filtrate. Then, hold the paper clip in the flame. Record the color you observe.

Reaction Observations	
Time (min)	**Observations**
5	
10	
15	
20	

CHEMLAB (3)

Cleanup and Disposal

1. Dispose of materials as directed by your teacher.

2. Clean and return all lab equipment to its proper place.

3. Wash hands thoroughly.

Analyze and Conclude

1. Classifying Which type of mixture is silver nitrate in water? Which type of mixture is formed in step 6? Explain.

_____

2. Observing and Inferring Describe the changes you observed in step 6. Is there evidence a chemical change occurred? Why?

_____

3. Predicting Predict the products formed in step 6. You may not know the exact chemical name, but you should be able to make an intuitive prediction.

_____

4. Using Resources Use resources such as the *CRC Handbook of Chemistry and Physics*, the *Merck Index*, or the Internet to determine the colors of silver metal and copper nitrate in water. Compare this information with your observations of the reactants and products in step 6.

_____

5. Identifying Metals emit characteristic colors in flame tests. Copper emits a blue-green light. Do your observations in step 12 confirm the presence of copper in the filtrate collected in step 9?

_____

6. Communicating Express in words the chemical equation that represents the reaction that occurred in step 6.

_____

7. Error Analysis Compare your recorded observations with those of several other lab teams. Explain any differences.

_____

Real-World Chemistry

1. Analytical chemists determine the chemical composition of matter. Two major branches of analytical chemistry are qualitative analysis—determining what is in a substance—and quantitative analysis—measuring how much substance. Research and report on a career as an analytical chemist in the food industry.

_____

Copyright © Glencoe/McGraw-Hill, a division of the McGraw-Hill Companies, Inc.

miniLAB 4

Modeling Isotopes

Formulating Models Because they have different compositions, pre- and post-1982 pennies can be used to model an element with two naturally occurring isotopes. From the penny "isotope" data, the mass of each penny isotope and the average mass of a penny can be determined.

Materials bag of pre- and post-1982 pennies, balance

Procedure

1. Get a bag of pennies from your teacher, and sort the pennies by date into two groups: pre-1982 pennies and post-1982 pennies. Count and record the total number of pennies and the number of pennies in each group.

2. Use the balance to determine the mass of ten pennies from each group. Record each mass to the nearest 0.01 g. Divide the total mass of each group by ten to get the average mass of a pre- and post-1982 penny "isotope."

Analysis

1. Using data from step 1, calculate the percentage abundance of each group. To do this, divide the number of pennies in each group by the total number of pennies.

_____

_____

2. Using the percentage abundance of each "isotope" and data from step 2, calculate the atomic mass of a penny. To do this, use the following equation for each "isotope."

mass contribution = (% abundance)(mass)

Sum the mass contributions to determine the atomic mass.

_____

3. Would the atomic mass be different if you received another bag of pennies containing a different mixture of pre- and post-1982 pennies? Explain.

_____

_____

4. In step 2, instead of measuring and using the mass of a single penny of each group, the average mass of each type of penny was determined. Explain why.

_____

_____

CHEMLAB ④

Very Small Particles

This laboratory investigation will help you conceptualize the size of an atom. You will experiment with a latex balloon containing a vanilla bean extract. Latex is a polymer, meaning that it is a large molecule (a group of atoms that act as a unit) that is made up of a repeating pattern of smaller molecules. The scent of the vanilla extract will allow you to trace the movement of its molecules through the walls of the solid latex balloon.

Problem

How small are the atoms that make up the molecules of the balloon and the vanilla extract? How can you conclude the vanilla molecules are in motion?

Objectives

- **Observe** the movement of vanilla molecules based on detecting their scent.
- **Infer** what the presence of the vanilla scent means in terms of the size and movement of its molecules.
- **Formulate models** that explain how small molecules in motion can pass through an apparent solid.
- **Hypothesize** about the size of atoms that make up matter.

Materials

vanilla extract or flavoring
9-inch latex balloon (2)
dropper

Safety Precautions

- **Always wear safety goggles and a lab apron.**
- **Be careful not to cut yourself when using a sharp object to deflate the balloon.**

Pre-Lab

1. Read the entire **CHEMLAB.**

2. Describe a polymer and give an example.

_____

_____

_____

_____

3. Identify constants in the experiment.

_____

_____

_____

CHEMLAB ④

4. What is the purpose of the vanilla extract?

_____

_____

_____

_____

5. As a liquid evaporates, predict what you think will happen to the temperature of the remaining liquid.

_____

_____

_____

6. When you smell an aroma, is your nose detecting a particle in the solid, liquid, or gas phase?

_____

7. Prepare all written materials that you will take into the laboratory. Be sure to include safety precautions and procedure notes. Use the data table below to record your data and observations.

Procedure

1. Using the dropper, add 25 to 30 drops of vanilla extract to the first balloon.

2. Inflate the balloon so its walls are tightly stretched, but not stretched so tightly that the

balloon is in danger of bursting. Try to keep the vanilla in one location as the balloon is inflated. Tie the balloon closed.

3. Feel the outside of the balloon where the vanilla is located and note the temperature of this area relative to the rest of the balloon. Record your observations in the data table.

4. Use only air to inflate a second balloon to approximately the same size as that of the first, and tie it closed. Feel the outside of the second balloon. Make a relative temperature comparison to that of the first balloon. Record your initial observations.

5. Place the inflated balloons in a small, enclosed area such as a closet or student locker.

6. The next day, repeat the observations in steps 3 and 4 after the vanilla has dried inside the balloon. Record these final observations.

7. To avoid splattering your clothes with dark brown vanilla, do not deflate the balloon until the vanilla has dried inside.

Cleanup and Disposal

1. After the vanilla has dried, deflate the balloon by puncturing it with a sharp object.

2. Dispose of the pieces of the balloon as directed by your teacher.

Data Table			Initial	Final
Observations				
Balloon 1 with vanilla	Relative size			
	Relative temperature			
Balloon 2 without vanilla	Relative size			
	Relative temperature			

Analyze and Conclude

1. Observing and Inferring How did the relative volumes of balloons 1 and 2 change after 24 hours?

_____

2. Observing and Inferring By comparing the relative temperatures of balloons 1 and 2, what can you conclude about the temperature change as the vanilla evaporated? Explain.

_____

_____

3. Observing and Inferring Did the vanilla's odor get outside the balloon and fill the enclosed space? Explain.

_____

_____

_____

4. Predicting Do you think vanilla will leak more rapidly from a fully inflated balloon or from a half-inflated balloon? Explain.

_____

_____

_____

5. Hypothesizing Write a hypothesis that explains your observations.

_____

6. Comparing and Contrasting Compare your hypothesis to Dalton's atomic theory. In what ways is it similar? How is it different?

_____

_____

_____

7. Error Analysis What factors might affect the results of different groups that performed the experiment? What types of errors might have occurred during the procedure?

_____

_____

Real-World Chemistry

1. Explain why helium-filled, Mylar-foil balloons can float freely for several weeks, but latex balloons for less than 24 hours.

_____

_____

2. How are high-pressure gases stored for laboratory and industrial use to prevent loss?

_____

miniLAB 5

Flame Tests

Classifying When certain compounds are heated in a flame, they emit a distinctive color. The color of the emitted light can be used to identify the compound.

Materials Bunsen burner; cotton swabs (6); distilled water; crystals of lithium chloride, sodium chloride, potassium chloride, calcium chloride, strontium chloride, unknown

Procedure

1. Dip a cotton swab into the distilled water. Dip the moistened swab into the lithium chloride so that a few of the crystals stick to the cotton. Put the crystals on the swab into the flame of a Bunsen burner. Observe the color of the flame and record it in the data table.

2. Repeat step 1 for each of the metallic chlorides (sodium chloride, potassium chloride, calcium chloride, and strontium chloride). Be sure to record the color of each flame in your data table.

3. Obtain a sample of unknown crystals from your teacher. Repeat the procedure in step 1 using the unknown crystals. Record the color of the flame produced by the unknown crystals in the data table. Dispose of used cotton swabs as directed by your teacher.

Flame Test Results	
Compound	**Flame color**
Lithium chloride	
Sodium chloride	
Potassium chloride	
Calcium chloride	
Strontium chloride	
Unknown	

Analysis

1. Each of the known compounds tested contains chlorine, yet each compound produced a flame of a different color. Explain why this occurred.

_____

_____

_____

2. How is the atomic emission spectrum of an element related to these flame tests?

_____

_____

_____

3. What is the identity of the unknown crystals? Explain how you know.

_____

_____

CHEMLAB 5

Line Spectra

You know that sunlight is made up of a continuous spectrum of colors that combine to form white light. You also have learned that atoms of gases can emit visible light of characteristic wavelengths when excited by electricity. The color you see is the sum of all of the emitted wavelengths. In this experiment, you will use a diffraction grating to separate these wavelengths into emission line spectra.

You also will investigate another type of line spectrum—the absorption spectrum. The color of each solution you observe is due to the reflection or transmission of unabsorbed wavelengths of light. When white light passes through a sample and then a diffraction grating, dark lines show up on the continuous spectrum of white light. These lines correspond to the wavelengths of the photons absorbed by the solution.

Problem

What absorption and emission spectra do various substances produce?

Objectives

- **Observe** emission spectra of several gases.
- **Observe** the absorption spectra of various solutions.
- **Analyze** patterns of absorption and emission spectra.

Materials

(For each group)
ring stand with clamp
40-W tubular light-bulb
light socket with power cord
275-mL polystyrene culture flask (4)
Flinn C-Spectra® or similar diffraction grating

food coloring (red, green, blue, and yellow)
set of colored pencils
book

(For entire class)
spectrum tubes (hydrogen, neon, and mercury)
spectrum tube power supplies (3)

Safety Precautions

- Always wear safety goggles and a lab apron.
- Use care around the spectrum tube power supplies.
- Spectrum tubes will get hot when used.

Pre-Lab

1. Read the entire **CHEMLAB**.

2. Explain how electrons in an element's atoms produce an emission spectrum.

_____   _____

_____   _____

_____   _____

_____   _____

Copyright © Glencoe/McGraw-Hill, a division of the McGraw-Hill Companies, Inc.

3. Distinguish among a continuous spectrum, an emission spectrum, and an absorption spectrum.

_____

_____

_____

_____

_____

_____

_____

4. Use the data tables below and on the next page.

Procedure

1. Use a Flinn C-Spectra® to view an incandescent lightbulb. What do you observe? Draw the spectrum using colored pencils.

2. Use the Flinn C-Spectra® to view the emission spectra from tubes of gaseous hydrogen, neon, and mercury. Use colored pencils to make drawings in the data table of the spectra observed.

3. Fill a 275-mL culture flask with about 100-mL water. Add 2 or 3 drops of red food coloring to the water. Shake the solution.

4. Repeat step 3 for the green, blue, and yellow food coloring. **CAUTION:** *Be sure to thoroughly dry your hands before handling electrical equipment.*

5. Set up the 40-W lightbulb so that it is near eye level. Place the flask with red food coloring about 8 cm from the lightbulb. Use a book or some other object to act as a stage to put the flask on. You should be able to see light from the bulb above the solution and light from the bulb projecting through the solution.

6. With the room lights darkened, view the light using the Flinn C-Spectra®. The top spectrum viewed will be a continuous spectrum of the white lightbulb. The bottom spectrum will be the absorption spectrum of the red solution. The black areas of the absorption spectrum represent the colors absorbed by the red food coloring in the solution. Use colored pencils to make a drawing in the data table of the absorption spectra you observed.

7. Repeat steps 5 and 6 using the green, blue, and yellow colored solutions.

Cleanup and Disposal

1. Turn off the light socket and spectrum tube power supplies.

2. Wait several minutes to allow the incandescent lightbulb and the spectrum tubes to cool.

3. Follow your teacher's instructions on how to dispose of the liquids and how to store the lightbulb and spectrum tubes.

Drawings of Emission Spectra	
Hydrogen	
Neon	
Mercury	

CHEMLAB 5

Drawings of Absorption Spectra	
Red	
Green	
Blue	
Yellow	

Analyze and Conclude

1. **Thinking Critically** How can the existence of spectra help to prove that energy levels in atoms exist?

   _____

   _____

2. **Thinking Critically** How can the single electron in a hydrogen atom produce all of the lines found in its emission spectrum?

   _____

   _____

3. **Predicting** How can you predict the absorption spectrum of a solution by looking at its color?

   _____

   _____

4. **Thinking Critically** How can spectra be used to identify the presence of specific elements in a substance?

   _____

   _____

Real-World Chemistry

1. How can absorption and emission spectra be used by the Hubble space telescope to study the structures of stars or other objects found in deep space?

   _____

   _____

2. The absorption spectrum of chlorophyll *a* indicates strong absorption of red and blue wavelengths. Explain why leaves appear green.

   _____

   _____

miniLAB 6

Periodicity of Molar Heats of Fusion and Vaporization

Making and Using Graphs The heats required to melt or to vaporize a mole (a specific amount of matter) of matter are known as the molar heat of fusion (H_f) and the molar heat of vaporization (H_v), respectively. These heats are unique properties of each element. You will investigate if the molar heats of fusion and vaporization for the period 2 and 3 elements behave in a periodic fashion.

Materials either a graphing calculator, a computer graphing program, or graph paper; Appendix **Table C-6** or access to comparable element data references

Procedure

Use **Table C-6** in Appendix C to look up and record the molar heat of fusion and the molar heat of vaporization for the period 3 elements listed in the table. Then, record the same data for the period 2 elements.

Analysis

1. Graph molar heats of fusion versus atomic number. Connect the points with straight lines and label the curve. Do the same for molar heats of vaporization.

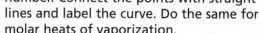

Molar Heat Data			
Element	Atomic number	H_f (kJ/mol)	H_v (kJ/mol)
Li	3		
Be	4		
B	5		
C	6		
N	7		
O	8		
F	9		
Ne	10		
Na	11		
Mg	12		
Al	13		
Si	14		
P	15		
S	16		
Cl	17		
Ar	18		

2. Do the graphs repeat in a periodic fashion? Describe the graphs to support your answer.

_____

_____

CHEMLAB 6

Descriptive Chemistry of the Elements

What do elements look like? How do they behave? Can periodic trends in the properties of elements be observed? You cannot examine all of the elements on the periodic table because of limited availability, cost, and safety concerns. However, you can observe several of the representative elements, classify them, and compare their properties. The observation of the properties of elements is called descriptive chemistry.

Problem

What is the pattern of properties of the representative elements?

Objectives

- **Observe** properties of various elements.
- **Classify** elements as metals, nonmetals, and metalloids.
- **Examine** general trends within the periodic table.

Materials

stoppered test tubes containing small samples of elements
plastic dishes containing samples of elements
conductivity apparatus

1.0*M* HCl
test tubes (6)
test-tube rack
10-mL graduated cylinder
spatula
small hammer
glass marking pencil

Safety Precautions

- Wear safety goggles and a lab apron at all times.
- Do not handle elements with bare hands.
- 1.0*M* HCl is harmful to eyes and clothing.
- Never test chemicals by tasting.
- Follow any additional safety precautions provided by your teacher.

Pre-Lab

1. Read the entire **CHEMLAB**.

2. Use the data table on the next page to record the observations you make during the lab.

3. Examine the periodic table. What is the physical state of most metals? Nonmetals? Metalloids?

_____

_____

_____

_____

4. Look up the definitions of the terms luster, malleability, and electrical conductivity. To what elements do they apply?

_____

_____

_____

_____

_____

_____

CHEMLAB ⑥

Procedure

1. Observe and record the appearance of the element sample in each test tube. Observations should include physical state, color, and other characteristics such as luster and texture. **CAUTION:** *Do not remove the stoppers from the test tubes.*

2. Remove a small sample of each of the elements contained in a dish and place it on a hard surface designated by your teacher. Gently tap each element sample with a small hammer. **CAUTION:** *Safety goggles must be worn.* If the element is malleable, it will flatten. If it is brittle, it will shatter. Record your observations.

3. Use the conductivity tester to determine which elements conduct electricity. An illuminated light-bulb is evidence of electrical conductivity. Record your results in your data table. Clean the electrodes with water and make sure they are dry before testing each element.

4. Label each test tube with the symbol for one of the elements in the plastic dishes. Using a graduated cylinder, add 5 mL of water to each test tube.

5. Use a spatula to put a small amount of each of the six elements (approximately 0.2 g or a 1-cm long ribbon) into the test tube labeled with its chemical symbol. Using a graduated cylinder, add 5 mL of 1.0*M* HCl to each test tube. Observe each test tube for at least one minute. The formation of bubbles is evidence of a reaction between the acid and the element. Record your observations.

Cleanup and Disposal

Dispose of all materials as instructed by your teacher.

Observation of Elements					
Element	Appearance and physical state	Malleable or brittle?	Reactivity with HCl	Electrical conductivity	Classification

Analyze and Conclude

1. Interpreting Data Metals are usually malleable and good conductors of electricity. They are generally lustrous and silver or white in color. Many react with acids. Write the word "metal" beneath the Classification heading in the data table for those element samples that display the general characteristics of metals.

2. Interpreting Data Nonmetals can be solids, liquids, or gases. They do not conduct electricity and do not react with acids. If a nonmetal is a solid, it is likely to be brittle and have color (other than white or silver). Write the word "nonmetal" beneath the Classification heading in the data table for those element samples that display the general characteristics of nonmetals.

CHEMLAB 6

3. **Interpreting Data** Metalloids combine some of the properties of both metals and non-metals. Write the word "metalloid" beneath the Classification heading in the data table for those element samples that display the general characteristics of metalloids.

4. **Making a Model** Construct a periodic table and label the representative elements by group (1A through 7A). Using the information in your data table and the periodic table, record the identities of elements observed during the lab in your periodic table.

_____

5. **Interpreting** Describe any trends among the elements you observed in the lab.

_____

_____

Real-World Chemistry

1. Why did it take so long to discover the first noble gas element?

_____

_____

_____

_____

2. Research one of the most recently discovered elements. New elements are created in particle accelerators and tend to be very unstable. Because of this, many of the properties of a new element cannot be determined. Using periodic group trends in melting and boiling point, predict whether the new element you selected is likely to be a solid, liquid, or gas.

_____

_____

_____

miniLAB 7
Properties of Magnesium

Observing and Inferring In this activity, you will mix magnesium with hydrochloric acid and observe the result.

Materials test tube, test-tube rack, 10-mL graduated cylinder, hydrochloric acid, magnesium ribbon, sandpaper, cardboard, wood splint, safety matches

Procedure
Record all of your observations.

1. Place your test tube in a test-tube rack. For safety, the test tube should remain in the rack throughout the lab.

2. Use a 10-mL graduated cylinder to measure out about 6 mL of hydrochloric acid. Pour the acid slowly into the test tube. **CAUTION:** *If acid gets on your skin, flush with cold running water. Use the eyewash station if acid gets in your eye.*

3. Use sandpaper to clean the surface of a 3-cm length of magnesium ribbon.

4. Drop the ribbon into the acid and immediately cover the test tube with a cardboard lid.

5. As the reaction appears to slow down, light a wood splint in preparation for step 6.

6. As soon as the reaction stops, uncover the test tube and drop the burning splint into it.

7. Pour the contents of the test tube into a container specified by your teacher. Then rinse the test tube with water. Do not place your fingers inside the unwashed tube.

Analysis

1. Compare the appearance of the magnesium ribbon before and after you used the sandpaper. What did the sandpaper remove?

_____

_____

2. What happened when you placed the ribbon in the acid? How did you decide when the reaction was over?

_____

_____

3. What did you observe when you placed the burning splint in the test tube?

_____

_____

4. What gas can ignite explosively when exposed to oxygen in the air? (Hint: The gas is lighter than air.)

_____

CHEMLAB 7

Hard Water

The contents of tap water vary among communities. In some areas, the water is hard. Hard water is water that contains large amounts of calcium or magnesium ions. Hardness can be measured in milligrams per liter (mg/L) of calcium or magnesium ions. Hard water makes it difficult to get hair, clothes, and dishes clean. In this lab, you will learn how hard water is softened and how softening water affects its ability to clean. You will also collect, test, and classify local sources of water.

Problem

How can hard water be softened? How do hard and soft water differ in their ability to clean?

Objectives

- **Compare** the effect of distilled water, hard water, and soft water on the production of suds.
- **Calculate** the hardness of a water sample.

Materials

3 large test tubes with stoppers
test-tube rack
grease pencil
25-mL graduated cylinder
distilled water
dropper

hard water
250-mL beaker
balance
filter paper
washing soda
dish detergent
metric ruler

Safety Precautions

- **Always wear safety goggles and a lab apron.**
- **Washing soda is a skin and eye irritant.**

Pre-Lab

1. Read the entire **CHEMLAB.**

2. Hypothesize about the effect hard and soft water will have on the ability of a detergent to produce suds. Then, predict the relative sudsiness of the three soap solutions.

_____

_____

_____

_____

_____

3. Use the data table on the next page.

4. Are there any other safety precautions you need to consider?

_____

_____

_____

5. Suppose you accidentally add more than one drop of detergent to one of the test tubes. Is there a way to adjust for this error or must you discard the sample and start over?

_____

_____

_____

_____

6. The American Society of Agricultural Engineers, the U.S. Department of the Interior, and the Water Quality Association agree on the following classification of water hardness. GPG stands for grains per gallon. One GPG equals 17.1 mg/L. If a sample of water has 150 mg/L of magnesium ions, what is its hardness in grains per gallon?

Classification of Water Hardness		
Classification	**mg/L**	**GPG**
Soft	0–60	0–3.5
Moderate	61–120	3.5–7
Hard	121–180	7–10.5
Very hard	> 180	> 10.5

Procedure

1. Use a grease pencil to label three large test tubes D (for distilled water), H (for hard water), and S (for soft water).

2. Use a 25-mL graduated cylinder to measure out 20-mL of distilled water. Pour the water into test tube D. Stopper the tube.

3. Place test tube H next to test tube D and make a mark on test tube H that corresponds to the height of the water in test tube D. Repeat the procedure with test tube S.

4. Obtain about 50-mL of hard water in a beaker from your teacher. Slowly pour hard water into test tube H until you reach the marked height.

5. Place a piece of filter paper on a balance and set the balance to zero. Then measure about 0.2 g of washing soda. Remove the filter paper and washing soda. Reset the balance to zero.

6. Use the filter paper to transfer the washing soda to the beaker containing the remainder of the hard water. Swirl the mixture to soften the water. Record any observations.

7. Slowly pour soft water into test tube S until you reach the marked height.

8. Add one drop of dish detergent to each test tube. Stopper the tubes tightly. Then shake each sample to produce suds. Use a metric ruler to measure the height of the suds.

9. Collect water samples from reservoirs, wells, or rain barrels. Use the sudsiness test to determine the hardness of your samples. If access to a source is restricted, ask a local official to collect the sample.

Cleanup and Disposal

1. Use some of the soapy solutions to remove the grease marks from the test tubes.

2. Rinse all of the liquids down the drain with lots of tap water.

Production of Suds	
Sample	**Level of Suds (cm)**
Distilled water	
Hard water	
Soft water	

Analyze and Conclude

1. Comparing and Contrasting Which sample produced the most suds? Which sample produced the least suds? Set up your own water hardness scale based on your data. What is the relative hardness of the local water samples?

_____

_____

_____

CHEMLAB ⑦

2. Using Numbers The hard water you used was prepared by adding 1 gram of magnesium sulfate per liter of distilled water. Magnesium sulfate contains 20.2% magnesium ions by mass. What is its hardness in grains per gallon?

_____

_____

3. Drawing a Conclusion The compound in washing soda is sodium carbonate. How did the sodium carbonate soften the hard water?

_____

_____

4. Thinking Critically Remember that most compounds of alkaline earth metals do not dissolve easily in water. What is the white solid that formed when washing soda was added to the solution of magnesium sulfate?

_____

5. Error Analysis Could the procedure be changed to make the results more quantitative? Explain.

_____

_____

Real-World Chemistry

1. Water softeners for washing machines are sold in the detergent section of a store. Look at some of the packages and compare ingredients. Do packages that have different ingredients also have different instructions for how the water softener should be used?

_____

2. Suppose a family notices that the water pressure in their house is not good enough to flush a toilet on the second floor. Other than a leak, what could be interfering with the flow of water?

_____

_____

3. Explain why drinking hard water might be better for your health than drinking soft water. How could a family have the benefit of hard water for drinking and soft water for washing?

_____

_____

miniLAB 8

Heat Treatment of Steel

Recognizing Cause and Effect People have treated metals with heat for many centuries. Different properties result when the metal is slowly or rapidly cooled. Can you determine how and why the properties change?

Materials laboratory burner, forceps (2), hairpins (3), 250-mL beaker

Procedure

1. Examine a property of spring steel by trying to bend open one of the hairpins. Record your observations.

2. Hold each end of a hairpin with forceps. Place the curved central loop in the top of the burner's flame. When it turns red, pull it open into a straight piece of metal. Allow it to cool as you record your observations. Repeat this procedure for the remaining two hairpins. **CAUTION:** *Do not touch the hot metal.*

3. To make softened steel, use forceps to hold all three hairpins vertically in the flame until they glow red all over. Slowly raise the three hairpins straight up and out of the flame so they cool slowly. Slow cooling results in the formation of large crystals.

4. After cooling, bend each of the three hairpins into the shape of the letter J. Record how the metal feels as you bend it.

5. To harden the steel, use tongs to hold two of the bent hairpins in the flame until they are glowing red all over. Quickly plunge the hot metals into a 250-mL beaker containing approximately 200 mL of cold water. Quick-cooling causes the crystal size to be small.

6. Attempt to straighten one of the bends. Record your observations.

7. To temper the steel, use tongs to briefly hold the remaining hardened metal bend above the flame. Slowly move the metal back and forth just above the flame until the gray metal turns to an iridescent blue-gray color. Do not allow the metal to glow red. Slowly cool the metal and then try to unbend it using the end of your finger. Record your observations.

Analysis

1. State a use for spring steel that takes advantage of its unique properties.

_____

2. What are the advantages and disadvantages of using softened steel for body panels on automobiles?

_____

3. What is the major disadvantage of hardened steel? Do you think this form of iron would be wear resistant and retain a sharpened edge?

_____

4. Which two types of steel appear to have their properties combined in tempered steel?

_____

5. State a hypothesis that explains how the different properties you have observed relate to crystal size.

_____
_____

Name _____ Date _____ Class _____

Making Ionic Compounds

Elements combine to form compounds. If energy is released as the compound is formed, the resulting product is more stable than the reacting elements. In this investigation, you will react elements to form two compounds. You will test the compounds to determine several of their properties. Ionic compounds have properties that are different from those of other compounds. You will decide if the products you formed are ionic compounds.

Problem

What are the formulas and names of the products that are formed? Do the properties of these compounds classify them as having ionic bonds?

Objectives

- **Observe** evidence of a chemical reaction.
- **Acquire** and **analyze** information that will enable you to decide if a compound has an ionic bond.
- **Classify** the products as ionic or not ionic.

Materials

magnesium ribbon
crucible
ring stand and ring
clay triangle
laboratory burner
stirring rod

crucible tongs
centigram balance
100-mL beaker
distilled water
conductivity tester

Safety Precautions

- Always wear safety glasses and a lab apron.
- Do not look directly at the burning magnesium. The intensity of the light can damage your eyes.
- Avoid handling heated materials until they have cooled.

Pre-Lab

1. Read the entire **CHEMLAB.** Identify the variable. List any conditions that must be kept constant.

_____

_____

2. Write the electron configuration of the magnesium atom.

_____

a. Based on this configuration, will magnesium lose or gain electrons to become a magnesium ion?

_____

b. Write the electron configuration of the magnesium ion.

_____

c. The magnesium ion has an electron configuration like that of which noble gas?

_____

3. Repeat question 2 for oxygen and nitrogen.

_____

_____

_____

CHEMLAB (8)

4. Use the data table in the next column.

5. In your data table, which mass values will be measured directly? Which mass values will be calculated?

_____

_____

_____

_____

6. Explain what must be done to calculate each mass value that is not measured directly.

_____

_____

_____

_____

_____

_____

_____

Procedure

1. Arrange the ring on the ring stand so that it is about 7 cm above the top of the Bunsen burner. Place the clay triangle on the ring.

2. Measure the mass of the clean, dry crucible, and record the mass in the data table.

3. Roll 25 cm of magnesium ribbon into a loose ball. Place it in the crucible. Measure the mass of the magnesium and crucible and record this mass in the data table.

4. Place the crucible on the clay ring. Heat the crucible with a hot flame, being careful to position the crucible near the top of the flame.

5. When the magnesium metal ignites and begins to burn with a bright white light, immediately turn off the laboratory burner. **CAUTION:** *Do not look directly at the burning magnesium.* After the magnesium product and crucible have cooled, measure their mass and record it in the data table.

6. Place the dry solid product in a small beaker for further testing.

7. Add 10 mL of distilled water to the dry magnesium product in the beaker and stir. Check the mixture with a conductivity checker, and record your results.

Mass Data	
Material(s)	**Mass (g)**
Empty crucible	
Crucible and Mg ribbon before heating	
Magnesium ribbon	
Crucible and magnesium products after heating	
Magnesium products	

Cleanup and Disposal

1. Wash out the crucible with water.

2. Dispose of the product as directed by your teacher.

3. Return all lab equipment to its proper place.

Analyze and Conclude

1. **Analyzing Data** Use the masses in the table to calculate the mass of the magnesium ribbon and the mass of the magnesium product. Record these masses in the table.

2. **Classifying** What kind of energy was released by the reaction? What can you conclude about the product of this reaction?

_____

_____

Name _____ Date _____ Class _____

3. Using Numbers How do you know that the magnesium metal reacts with certain components of the air?

_____

_____

4. Predicting Magnesium reacts with both oxygen and nitrogen from the air at the high temperature of the crucible. Predict the binary formulas for both products. Write the names of these two compounds.

_____

_____

5. Analyzing and Concluding The product formed from magnesium and oxygen is white, and the product formed from magnesium and nitrogen is yellow. From your observations, which compound makes up most of the product?

_____

_____

6. Analyzing and Concluding Did the magnesium compounds and water conduct an electric current? Do the results indicate whether or not the compounds are ionic?

_____

_____

7. Error Analysis If the magnesium lost mass instead of gaining mass, what do you think was a possible source of the error?

_____

_____

Real-World Chemistry

1. The magnesium ion plays an important role in a person's biochemistry. Research the role of this electrolyte in your physical and mental health. Is magnesium listed as a component in a multivitamin and mineral tablet?

_____

_____

_____

2. Research the use of $Mg(OH)_2$ in everyday products. What is $Mg(OH)_2$ commonly called in over-the-counter drugs?

_____

_____

_____

miniLAB 9
Building VSEPR Models

Formulating Models The VSEPR model states that pairs of valence electrons on a central atom repel each other and are arranged so that the repulsions are as small as possible. In this **miniLAB,** you will use marshmallows and gumdrops to build models of substances, showing examples of the VSEPR model.

Materials regular-sized marshmallows (3); mini-sized marshmallows (9); small gumdrops (3); toothpicks, cut in half

Procedure

1. Draw Lewis structures for methane (CH_4), ammonia (NH_3), and water (H_2O). Notice the location of each shared and unshared pair of electrons.

2. Using your Lewis structures, build a VSEPR model for each molecule. Use a mini-marshmallow to represent both the hydrogen atom and the region of space containing the pair of electrons shared by hydrogen and the central atom. Use a regular-sized marshmallow to represent the space occupied by an unshared pair of electrons and a small gumdrop to represent a central atom. Use small pieces of toothpicks to attach the marshmallows and gumdrops to each other. Sketch each of your models.

Analysis

1. How did drawing a Lewis structure help you to determine the geometry of each of your substances?

_____

_____

_____

2. Why was a mini-marshmallow used to show a shared pair of electrons and a regular marshmallow an unshared pair?

_____

_____

_____

3. How can the VSEPR model help to predict the bond angles for these substances?

_____

_____

_____

CHEMLAB 9

Chromatography

Paper chromatography is a common way to separate various components of a mixture. The components of the mixture separate because different substances are selectively absorbed by paper due to differences in polarity. In this field or laboratory investigation, you will separate the various pigments found in leaves. You also will calculate the ratio called R_f for each of them. The ratio R_f compares the distance traveled by a substance, D_s, to the distance traveled by the solvent, D_f. The ratio is written as $R_f = D_s / D_f$.

Problem

How can a mixture be separated based on the polarity of substances in the mixture?

Objectives

- **Separate** pigments found in leaves.
- **Determine** the R_f value for each of the pigments in the leaves.

Materials

chromatography paper (3 pieces)
2-L plastic soft drink bottle
pencils (2)
metric ruler
tape
scissors or metal snips

aluminum foil
acetone
fresh leaf samples from three different species of deciduous trees or outdoor plants

Safety Precautions

- **Acetone is a flammable liquid. Do not use near flames or sparks.**
- **Do not allow acetone to contact skin.**
- **Perform procedure in an area with proper ventilation.**

Pre-Lab

1. Read the entire **CHEMLAB.**

2. Prepare all written materials that you will take into the laboratory. Be sure to include safety precautions and procedure notes. Use the data table on the next page to record your observations.

3. What is polarity? How is polarity related to how chromatography works?

_____

_____

_____

_____

_____

_____

4. Predict what will happen when a mixture of leaf pigments is placed on a piece of paper and a solvent is allowed to move through the paper, moving the pigment with it.

_____

_____

_____

_____

_____

_____

_____

_____

Copyright © Glencoe/McGraw-Hill, a division of the McGraw-Hill Companies, Inc.

CHEMLAB ⑨

5. Suppose that the pigments in two samples contain red pigment and that the red pigment in sample A is more soluble in acetone than the red pigment in sample B. Form a hypothesis regarding which red pigment has the higher R_f value. Explain your answer.

_____

_____

_____

_____

_____

Procedure

1. For each leaf sample, crush the leaves and soak them in a small amount of acetone to make a concentrated solution of the pigments in the leaves.

2. Cut the top off a 2-liter bottle. Cut small notches, as shown in the figure so that a pencil can rest across the top of the bottle.

3. Cut three pieces of 3-cm wide chromatography paper to a length of about 18 cm. Label the top of each paper with a number. Assign a number to each pigment sample used. Draw pencil lines about 5 cm from the bottom of the end of each paper.

4. On the pencil line of paper 1, put a dot from the first sample. Make sure the dot is concentrated

but not wide. Do the same for the other samples on their respective papers. Tape the papers to the pencil, as shown in the figure.

5. Put enough acetone in the 2-liter bottle so that when the papers are put in the bottle, the solvent touches only the bottom 1 cm of each paper, as shown in the figure. **CAUTION:** *Do not allow acetone to come in contact with skin. Use in area with proper ventilation.*

6. Carefully lower the chromatography papers into the acetone and put the pencil into the notches at the top of the bottle. Cover the top with aluminum foil. Allow the chromatograms to develop for about 35–40 minutes.

7. When the chromatograms are finished, remove them from the bottle. Mark the highest point reached by the solvent. Then, allow the papers to air dry.

Paper Chromatography				
Leaf sample	D_f (cm)	Colors	D_s (cm)	R_f
1				
2				
3				

Cleanup and Disposal

1. Dispose of the acetone as directed by your teacher.

2. Throw the chromatography paper in the trash can.

Analyze and Conclude

1. **Observing and Inferring** Record in the data table the colors that are found in each of the chromatograms. Space is allowed for three colors, but some samples may contain fewer or more than three colors.

2. **Measuring** For each strip, measure the distance the solvent traveled from the pencil line (D_f). For each color, measure from the top of the original marker dot to the farthest point the color traveled (D_s). Record these values in your data table.

3. **Interpreting Data** Calculate the R_f values for each of the pigments in each chromatogram and record them in the data table.

4. **Comparing and Contrasting** Describe the differences between the pigments in each of the samples.

_____

_____

5. **Applying Concepts** Will a polar solvent, such as water, cause a difference in how the pigments are separated? Explain your answer.

_____

_____

_____

6. **Error Analysis** What could be done to improve the measurements you used to calculate R_f?

_____

_____

Real-World Chemistry

1. Use your results to explain what happens to leaves in autumn.

_____

_____

2. How might chromatography be used to analyze the composition of the dye in a marker?

_____

_____

_____

miniLAB 10
Observing a Precipitate-Forming Reaction

Applying Concepts When two clear, colorless solutions are mixed, a chemical reaction may occur, resulting in the formation of a precipitate.

Materials 150-mL beakers (2); 100-mL graduated cylinder; stirring rod (2); spatula (2); weighing paper (2); NaOH; Epsom salts ($MgSO_4 \cdot 7H_2O$); distilled water; balance

Procedure

1. **CAUTION:** *Use gloves when working with NaOH.* Measure about 4 g NaOH and place it in a 150-mL beaker. Add 50 mL distilled water to the NaOH. Mix with a stirring rod until the NaOH dissolves.

2. Measure about 6 g Epsom salts and place it in another 150-mL beaker. Add 50 mL distilled water to the Epsom salts. Mix with another stirring rod until the Epsom salts dissolve.

3. Slowly pour the Epsom salts solution into the NaOH solution. Record your observations.

4. Stir the new solution. Record your observations.

5. Allow the precipitate to settle, then decant the liquid from the solid. Dispose of the solid as your teacher instructs.

Analysis

1. Write a chemical equation for the reaction between the NaOH and $MgSO_4$. Most sulfate compounds exist as ions in aqueous solutions.

   _____

2. Write the complete ionic equation for this reaction.

   _____

   _____

3. Write the net ionic equation for this reaction.

   _____

CHEMLAB 10

Activities of Metals

Some metals are more reactive than others. By comparing how different metals react with the same ions in aqueous solutions, an activity series for the tested metals can be developed. The activity series will reflect the relative reactivity of the tested metals. It can be used to predict whether reactions will occur.

Problem

Which is the most reactive metal tested? Which is the least reactive metal tested? Can this information be used to predict whether reactions will occur?

Objectives

- **Observe** chemical reactions.
- **Sequence** the activities of some metals.
- **Predict** if reactions will occur between certain substances.

Materials

1.0M Zn(NO$_3$)$_2$
1.0M Al(NO$_3$)$_3$
1.0M Cu(NO$_3$)$_2$
1.0M Mg(NO$_3$)$_2$
pipettes (4)
wire cutters
Cu wire

Al wire
Mg ribbon
Zn metal strips (4)
emery cloth or fine sandpaper
24-well microscale reaction plate

Safety Precautions

- **Always wear safety goggles and a lab apron.**
- **Use caution when using sharp and coarse equipment.**

Pre-Lab

1. Read the entire **CHEMLAB.**
2. Make notes about procedures and safety precautions to use in the laboratory.
3. Use the data table on the next page.
4. Form a hypothesis about what reactions will occur.

_____

_____

_____

_____

_____

5. What are the independent and dependent variables?

_____

_____

_____

_____

_____

6. What gas is produced when magnesium and hydrochloric acid react? Write the chemical equation for the reaction.

_____

_____

_____

Copyright © Glencoe/McGraw-Hill, a division of the McGraw-Hill Companies, Inc.

CHEMLAB 10

7. Why is it important to clean the magnesium ribbon? How might not polishing a piece of metal affect the reaction involving that metal?

_____

_____

_____

Procedure

1. Use a pipette to fill each of the four wells in column 1 of the reaction plate with 2 mL of $1.0M$ $Al(NO_3)_3$ solution.

2. Repeat the procedure in step 1 to fill the four wells in column 2 with 2 mL of $1.0M$ $Mg(NO_3)_2$ solution.

3. Repeat the procedure in step 1 to fill the four wells in column 3 with 2 mL of $1.0M$ $Zn(NO_3)_2$ solution.

4. Repeat the procedure in step 1 to fill the four wells in column 4 with 2 mL of $1.0M$ $Cu(NO_3)_2$ solution.

5. With the emery paper or sandpaper, polish 10 cm of aluminum wire until it is shiny. Use wire cutters to cut the aluminum wire into four 2.5-cm pieces. Place a piece of the aluminum wire in each row A well that contains solution.

6. Repeat the procedure in step 5 using 10 cm of magnesium ribbon. Place a piece of the Mg ribbon in each row B well that contains solution.

7. Use the emery paper or sandpaper to polish small strips of zinc metal. Place a piece of Zn metal in each row C well that contains solution.

8. Repeat the procedure in step 5 using 10 cm of copper wire. Place a piece of Cu wire in each row D well that contains solution.

9. Observe what happens in each cell. After 5 minutes, record your observations in the data table.

Reactions Between Solutions and Metals				
	$Al(NO_3)_3$	$Mg(NO_3)_2$	$Zn(NO_3)_2$	$Cu(NO_3)_2$
Al				
Mg				
Zn				
Cu				

Cleanup and Disposal

1. Dispose of all chemicals and solutions as directed by your teacher.

2. Clean your equipment and return it to its proper place.

3. Wash your hands thoroughly before you leave the lab.

Analyze and Conclude

1. Observing and Inferring In which wells of the reaction plate did chemical reactions occur? Which metal reacted with the most solutions? Which metal reacted with the fewest solutions? Which metal is the most reactive?

_____

_____

2. Sequencing The most active metal reacted with the most solutions. The least active metal reacted with the fewest solutions. Order the four metals from the most active to the least active.

_____

CHEMLAB 10

3. Comparing and Contrasting Compare your activity series with the activity series shown here. How does the order you determined for the four metals you tested compare with the order of these metals?

_____

4. Applying Concepts Write a chemical equation for each single-replacement reaction that occurred on your reaction plate.

_____
_____
_____
_____
_____

Most active ↓ **Least active**

METALS
Lithium
Rubidium
Potassium
Calcium
Sodium
Magnesium
Aluminum
Manganese
Zinc
Iron
Nickel
Tin
Lead
Copper
Silver
Platinum
Gold

Most active ↓ **Least active**

HALOGENS
Fluorine
Chlorine
Bromine
Iodine

5. Predicting Use the diagram to predict if a single-replacement reaction will occur between the following reactants. Write a chemical equation for each reaction that will occur.

a. Ca and $Sn(NO_3)_2$ _____

b. Ag and $Ni(NO_3)_2$ _____

c. Cu and $Pb(NO_3)_3$ _____

6. Error Analysis If the activity series you sequenced does not agree with the order in the diagram above, propose a reason for the disagreement.

_____
_____

Real-World Chemistry

1. Under what circumstances might it be important to know the activity tendencies of a series of elements?

_____
_____

2. Describe some of the environmental impacts of nitrates.

_____
_____

miniLAB 11

Percent Composition and Gum

Interpreting Data Water soluble sweeteners and flavorings are added to chewing gum. Are these chemicals added as an outside coating or are they mixed throughout the gum?

Materials balance, weighing paper, 250-mL beakers (2), pieces of chewing gum (2), stirring rod, paper towels, window screen (10 cm × 10 cm), scissors, clock or timer

Procedure

CAUTION: *Do not taste or eat any items used in the lab.*

1. Unwrap two pieces of chewing gum. Measure the mass of each separately on a piece of weighing paper. Label the weighing papers with the masses to avoid mixing up your data. Record the masses.

2. Add 150 mL of cold tap water to a 250-mL beaker. Place one piece of chewing gum in the water and stir for 2 minutes.

3. Remove the gum from the water and pat dry using paper towels. Measure and record the mass of the dried gum.

4. Use scissors to cut the second piece of gum into small pieces, each about the width of a pea. Repeat step 2 using fresh water. Use the stirring rod to keep the pieces of gum from clumping together.

5. Use the window screen to strain the water from the gum. Pat the gum dry using paper towels. Measure and record the mass of the dried gum.

6. Discard the gum in a waste container.

_____

Analysis

1. For the uncut piece of gum, calculate the mass of sweeteners and flavorings that dissolved in the water. The mass of sweeteners and flavorings is the difference between the original mass of the gum and the mass of the dried gum.

   _____

   _____

2. For the gum that was in small pieces, calculate the mass of dissolved sweeteners and flavorings.

   _____

   _____

3. For both pieces of gum, calculate the percent of the original mass that was soluble sweeteners and flavorings. For help, refer to *Percents* in the **Math Handbook** on page 909 of your textbook.

   _____

   _____

4. What can you infer from the two percentages? Is the gum sugar-coated or are the sweeteners and flavorings mixed throughout?

   _____

   _____

CHEMLAB 11

Hydrated Crystals

Hydrates are compounds that incorporate water molecules in their crystalline structures. The ratio of moles of water to one mole of the compound is a small whole number. For example, in the hydrated compound copper(II) sulfate pentahydrate ($CuSO_4 \cdot 5H_2O$), the ratio is 5:1. The ratio of moles of water to one mole of a hydrate can be determined experimentally by heating the hydrate to remove water.

Problem

How can you determine the moles of water in a mole of a hydrated compound?

Objectives

- **Heat** a known mass of hydrated compound until the water is removed.
- **Calculate** the formula for a hydrate using the mass of the hydrated compound and the mass of the anhydrous compound.

Materials

Bunsen burner
ring stand and ring
crucible and lid
clay triangle
crucible tongs
balance
Epsom salts (hydrated $MgSO_4$)
spatula
spark lighter or matches

Safety Precautions

- **Always wear safety goggles and a lab apron.**
- **Hot objects will not appear to be hot.**
- **Use the Bunsen burner carefully.**
- **Turn off the Bunsen burner when not in use.**

Pre-Lab

1. Read the entire **CHEMLAB**.

2. Prepare all written materials that you will take into the laboratory. Be sure to include safety precautions and procedure notes. Use the data table on the next page.

3. Explain how you will obtain the mass of water and the mass of anhydrous $MgSO_4$ contained in the hydrate.

_____

_____

_____

_____

_____

_____

4. How will you convert the masses of anhydrous $MgSO_4$ and water to moles?

_____

_____

_____

_____

5. How can you obtain the formula for the hydrate from the moles of anhydrous $MgSO_4$ and the moles of water?

_____

_____

_____

_____

Copyright © Glencoe/McGraw-Hill, a division of the McGraw-Hill Companies, Inc.

CHEMLAB 11

Mass Data and Observations of Epsom Salts	
Observations of hydrated $MgSO_4$	
Mass of crucible and lid	
Mass of crucible, lid, and hydrated $MgSO_4$	
Mass of hydrated $MgSO_4$	
Mass of crucible, lid, and anhydrous $MgSO_4$	
Mass of anhydrous $MgSO_4$	
Mass of water in hydrated $MgSO_4$	
Moles of anhydrous $MgSO_4$	
Moles of water in hydrated $MgSO_4$	
Observation of anhydrous $MgSO_4$	

Procedure

1. Measure to the nearest 0.01 g the mass of a clean, dry crucible with a lid. Record the mass.

2. Add about 3 g hydrated $MgSO_4$ to the crucible. Measure the mass of the crucible, lid, and hydrate to the nearest 0.01 g and record the mass.

3. Record your observations of the hydrate.

4. Place the triangle on the ring of the ring stand. Carefully place the crucible in the triangle.

5. Place the crucible lid on the crucible slightly cocked to help prevent spattering and allow vapor to escape. Begin heating with a low flame, then gradually progress to a stronger flame. Heat for about 10 minutes.

6. When heating is complete, remove the crucible using tongs. Place the lid on the crucible and allow the crucible and contents to cool.

7. Measure the mass of the crucible, lid, and $MgSO_4$ and record the mass in the data table.

8. Observe the anhydrous $MgSO_4$ and record your observations.

Cleanup and Disposal

1. Discard the anhydrous $MgSO_4$ in a trash container or as directed by your teacher.

2. Return all lab equipment to its proper place and clean your lab station.

3. Wash your hands thoroughly when all lab work and cleanup are complete.

Analyze and Conclude

1. Using Numbers Use your experimental data to calculate the formula for hydrated $MgSO_4$.

2. Observing and Inferring How did your observations of the hydrated $MgSO_4$ crystals compare with those of the anhydrous $MgSO_4$ crystals?

_____

_____

3. Drawing Conclusions Why might the method used in this experiment not be suitable for determining the water of hydration for all hydrates?

_____

4. **Error Analysis** What is the percent error of your calculation of the water of hydration for $MgSO_4$ if the formula for the hydrate is $MgSO_4 \cdot 7H_2O$? What changes would you make in the procedure to reduce error?

_____

_____

5. Predicting What might you observe if the anhydrous crystals were left uncovered overnight?

_____

Real-World Chemistry

1. Packets of the anhydrous form of a hydrate are sometimes used to keep cellars from being damp. Is there a limit to how long a packet could be used?

_____

_____

2. Gypsum ($CaSO_4 \cdot 2H_2O$) is a mineral used for making wallboard for construction. The mineral is stripped of three-quarters of its water of hydration in a process called calcining. Then, after mixing with water, it hardens to a white substance called plaster of paris. Infer what happens as calcined gypsum becomes plaster of paris.

_____

_____

miniLAB 12

Baking Soda Stoichiometry

Predicting When baking soda is an ingredient in your recipe, its purpose is to make the batter rise and produce a product with a light and fluffy texture. That's because baking soda, or sodium hydrogen carbonate ($NaHCO_3$), decomposes upon heating to form carbon dioxide gas.

$$2NaHCO_3 \rightarrow Na_2CO_3 + CO_2 + H_2O$$

Predict how much sodium carbonate (Na_2CO_3) is produced when baking soda decomposes.

Materials ring stand, ring, clay triangle, crucible, crucible tongs, Bunsen burner, balance, 3.0 g baking soda ($NaHCO_3$)

Procedure

1. Measure the mass of a clean, dry crucible. Add about 3.0 g of $NaHCO_3$ and measure the combined mass of the crucible and $NaHCO_3$. Record both masses and calculate the mass of the $NaHCO_3$.

   _____

   _____

2. Use this starting mass of baking soda and the balanced chemical equation to calculate the mass of Na_2CO_3 that will be produced.

   _____

   _____

3. Set up a ring stand with a ring and clay triangle for heating the crucible.

4. Heat the crucible slowly at first and then with a stronger flame for 7–8 min. Use tongs to remove the hot crucible. Record your observations during the heating.

5. Allow the crucible to cool and then obtain the mass of the crucible and sodium carbonate.

_____

Analysis

1. What were your observations during the heating of the baking soda?

   _____

   _____

2. How did your calculated mass of sodium carbonate compare with the actual mass you obtained from the experiment? If the two masses are different, suggest reasons for the difference.

   _____

   _____

CHEMLAB 12

A Mole Ratio

Iron reacts with copper(II) sulfate in a single replacement reaction. By measuring the mass of iron that reacts and the mass of copper metal produced, you can calculate the ratio of moles of reactant to moles of product. This mole ratio can be compared to the ratio found in the balanced chemical equation.

Problem

Which reactant is the limiting reactant? How does the experimental mole ratio of Fe to Cu compare with the mole ratio in the balanced chemical equation? What is the percent yield?

Objectives

- **Observe** a single replacement reaction.
- **Measure** the masses of iron and copper.
- **Calculate** the moles of each metal and the mole ratio.

Materials

iron metal filings, 20 mesh
copper(II) sulfate pentahydrate ($CuSO_4 \cdot 5H_2O$)
distilled water
stirring rod
150-mL beaker

400-mL beaker
100-mL graduated cylinder
weighing paper
balance
hot plate
beaker tongs

Safety Precautions

- **Always wear safety glasses and a lab apron.**
- **Hot objects will not appear to be hot.**
- **Do not heat broken, chipped, or cracked glassware.**
- **Turn off the hot plate when not in use.**

Pre-Lab

1. Read the entire **CHEMLAB.**

2. Prepare all written materials that you will take into the laboratory. Be sure to include safety precautions and procedure notes. Use the data table on the next page.

3. Is it important that you know you are using the hydrated form of copper(II) sulfate? Would it be possible to use the anhydrous form? Why or why not?

_____

_____

_____

_____

_____

_____

Procedure

1. Measure and record the mass of a clean, dry 150-mL beaker.

2. Place approximately 12 g of copper(II) sulfate pentahydrate into the 150-mL beaker and measure and record the combined mass.

3. Add 50 mL of distilled water to the copper(II) sulfate pentahydrate and heat the mixture on the hot plate at a medium setting. Stir until all of the solid is dissolved, but do not boil. Using tongs, remove the beaker from the hot plate.

4. Measure approximately 2 g of iron metal filings onto a piece of weighing paper. Measure and record the exact mass of the filings.

5. While stirring, slowly add the iron filings to the hot copper(II) sulfate solution.

6. Allow the reaction mixture to stand, without stirring, for 5 minutes to ensure complete reaction. The solid copper metal will settle to the bottom of the beaker.

Copyright © Glencoe/McGraw-Hill, a division of the McGraw-Hill Companies, Inc.

CHEMLAB 12

7. Use the stirring rod to decant (pour off) the liquid into a 400-mL beaker. Be careful to decant only the liquid.

8. Add 15 mL of distilled water to the copper solid and carefully swirl the beaker to wash the copper. Decant the liquid into the 400-mL beaker.

9. Repeat step 8 two more times.

10. Place the 150-mL beaker containing the wet copper on the hot plate. Use low heat to dry the copper.

11. Remove the beaker from the hot plate and allow it to cool.

12. Measure and record the mass of the cooled 150-mL beaker and the copper.

Cleanup and Disposal

1. Make sure the hot plate is off.

2. The dry copper can be placed in a waste container. Wet any residue that sticks to the beaker and wipe it out using a paper towel. Pour the unreacted copper(II) sulfate and iron(II) sulfate solutions into a large beaker in the fume hood.

3. Return all lab equipment to its proper place.

4. Wash your hands thoroughly after all lab work and cleanup is complete.

Data for the Reaction of Copper(II) Sulfate and Iron	
Mass of empty 150-mL beaker	
Mass of 150-mL beaker + $CuSO_4 \cdot 5H_2O$	
Mass of $CuSO_4 \cdot 5H_2O$	
Mass of iron filings	
Mass of 150-mL beaker and dried copper	
Mass of dried copper	
Observations	

Analyze and Conclude

1. **Observing and Inferring** What evidence did you observe that confirms that a chemical reaction occurred?

_____

2. **Applying Concepts** Write a balanced chemical equation for the single-replacement reaction that occurred.

_____

3. **Interpreting Data** From your data, determine the mass of copper produced.

_____

4. **Using Numbers** Use the mass of copper to calculate the moles of copper produced.

_____

5. **Using Numbers** Calculate the moles of iron used in the reaction.

_____

6. **Using Numbers** Determine the whole number ratio of moles of iron to moles of copper.

_____

7. **Comparing and Contrasting** Compare the ratio of moles of iron to moles of copper from the balanced chemical equation to the mole ratio calculated using your data.

_____

_____

8. **Evaluating Results** Use the balanced chemical equation to calculate the mass of copper that should have been produced from the sample of iron you used. Use this number and the mass of copper you actually obtained to calculate the percent yield.

_____

_____

9. **Error Analysis** What was the source of any deviation from the mole ratio calculated from the chemical equation? How could you improve your results?

_____

_____

_____

10. **Drawing a Conclusion** Which reactant is the limiting reactant? Explain.

_____

Real-World Chemistry

1. A furnace that provides heat by burning methane gas (CH_4) must have the correct mixture of air and fuel to operate efficiently. What is the mole ratio of air to methane gas in the combustion of methane? Hint: Air is 20% oxygen.

_____

_____

_____

2. Automobile air bags inflate on impact because a series of gas-producing chemical reactions are triggered. To be effective in saving lives, the bags must not overinflate or underinflate. What factors must automotive engineers take into account in the design of air bags?

_____

_____

_____

miniLAB 13
Crystal Unit Cell Models

Formulating Models You can make physical models that illustrate the structures of crystals.

Materials plastic or paper soda straws (12), 22- or 26-gauge wire, scissors

Procedure

1. Cut four soda straws into thirds. Wire the pieces to make a cube. All angles are 90°.
2. To model a rhombohedral crystal, deform the cube from step 1 until no angles are 90°.
3. To model a hexagonal crystal, flatten the model from step 2 until it looks like a pie with six slices.
4. To model a tetragonal crystal, cut four straws in half. Cut four of the pieces in half again. Wire the eight shorter pieces to make four square ends. Use the longer pieces to connect the square ends.
5. To model the orthorhombic crystal, cut four straws in half. Cut 1/3 off four of the halves. Connect the four long, four medium, and four short pieces so that each side is a rectangle.
6. To model the monoclinic crystal, deform the model from step 5 along one axis. To model the triclinic crystal, deform the model from step 5 until it has no 90° angles.

Analysis

1. Which two models have three axes of equal length? How do these models differ?

_____

_____

_____

2. Which model includes a square and rectangle?

_____

3. Which models have three unequal axes?

_____

_____

4. Do you think crystals are perfect or do they have defects? Explain your answer.

_____

_____

_____

CHEMLAB 13

Comparing Rates of Evaporation

Several factors determine how fast a sample of liquid will evaporate. The volume of the sample is a key factor. A drop of water takes less time to evaporate than a liter of water. The amount of energy supplied to the sample is another factor. In this lab, you will investigate how the type of liquid and temperature affect the rate of evaporation.

Problem
How do intermolecular forces affect the evaporation rates of liquids?

Objectives
- **Measure** and **compare** the rates of evaporation for different liquids.
- **Classify** liquids based on their rates of evaporation.
- **Predict** which intermolecular forces exist between the particles of each liquid.

Materials
distilled water
ethanol
isopropyl alcohol
acetone
household
  ammonia
droppers (5)
small plastic cups (5)

grease pencil or
  masking tape and
  a marking pen
paper towel
square of waxed
  paper
stopwatch

Safety Precautions

- **Always wear safety goggles and a lab apron.**
- **Wear gloves because some of the liquids can dry out your skin.**
- **Avoid inhaling any of the vapors, especially ammonia.**
- **There should be no open flames in the lab; some of the liquids are flammable.**

Pre-Lab

1. Read the entire **CHEMLAB.** Use the data table on the next page.

2. What is evaporation? Describe what happens at the molecular level during evaporation.

   _____

   _____

   _____

   _____

   _____

3. List the three possible intermolecular forces. Which force is the weakest? Which force is the strongest?

   _____

   _____

   _____

4. Look at the materials list for this lab. Consider the five liquids you will test. Predict which liquids will evaporate quickly and which will take longer to evaporate. Give reasons for your predictions.

   _____

   _____

   _____

   _____

   _____

5. To calculate an evaporation rate, you would divide the evaporation time by the quantity of liquid used. Explain why it is possible to use the evaporation times from this lab as evaporation rates.

_____

_____

_____

6. Make sure you know how to use the stopwatch provided. Will you need to convert the reading on the stopwatch to seconds?

Procedure

1. Use a grease pencil or masking tape to label each of five small plastic cups. Use A for distilled water, B for ethanol, C for isopropyl alcohol, D for acetone, and E for household ammonia.

2. Place the plastic cups on a paper towel.

3. Use a dropper to collect about 1 mL of distilled water and place the water in the cup labeled A. Place the dropper on the paper towel directly in front of the cup. Repeat with the other liquids.

4. Place a square of waxed paper on your lab surface. Plan where on the waxed paper you will place each of the 5 drops that you will test. The

drops must be as far apart as possible to avoid mixing.

5. Have your stopwatch ready. Collect some water in your water dropper and place a single drop on the waxed paper. Begin timing. Time how long it takes for the drop to completely evaporate. While you wait, make two drawings of the drop. One drawing should show the shape of the drop as viewed from above. The other drawing should be a side view at eye level. If the drop takes longer than 5 minutes to evaporate, record > 300 in your data table.

6. Repeat step 5 with the four other liquids.

7. Use the above procedure to design an experiment in which you can observe the effect of temperature on the rate of evaporation of ethanol. Your teacher will provide a sample of warm ethanol. Record your observations.

Cleanup and Disposal

1. Crumple up the waxed paper and place it in the container assigned by your teacher.

2. Place unused liquids in the containers specified by your teacher.

3. Wash out all droppers and test tubes except those used for distilled water.

Evaporation Data		
Liquid	**Evaporation time (s)**	**Shape of liquid drop**
Distilled water		
Ethanol		
Ethanol (warm)		
Isopropyl alcohol		
Acetone		
Household ammonia		

Analyze and Conclude

1. Classifying Which liquids evaporated quickly? Which liquids were slow to evaporate?

_____

CHEMLAB 13

2. **Drawing a Conclusion** Based on your data, in which liquid(s) are the attractive forces between molecules most likely to be dispersion forces?

_____

3. **Interpreting Data** Make a generalization about the shape of a liquid drop and the evaporation rate of the liquid.

_____

4. **Recognizing Cause and Effect** What is the relationship between surface tension and the shape of a liquid drop? What are the attractive forces that increase surface tension?

_____

5. **Applying Concepts** The isopropyl alcohol you used is a mixture of isopropyl alcohol and water. Would pure isopropyl alcohol evaporate more quickly or more slowly compared to the alcohol and water mixture? Give a reason for your answer.

_____

6. **Thinking Critically** Household ammonia is a mixture of ammonia and water. Based on the data you collected, is there more ammonia or more water in the mixture? Use what you learned about the relative strengths of the attractive forces in ammonia and water to support your conclusion.

_____

7. **Drawing a Conclusion** How does the rate of evaporation of warm ethanol compare to ethanol at room temperature? Use kinetic-molecular theory to explain your observations.

_____

8. **Error Analysis** How could you change the procedure to make it more precise?

_____

Real-World Chemistry

1. The vapor phases of liquids such as acetone and alcohol are more flammable than their liquid phases. For flammable liquids, what is the relationship between evaporation rate and the likelihood that the liquid will burn?

_____

2. Suggest why a person who has a higher than normal temperature might be given a rubdown with rubbing alcohol (70% isopropyl alcohol).

_____

3. Table salt can be collected from salt water by evaporation. The water is placed in large, shallow containers. What advantage do these shallow containers have over deep containers with the same overall volume?

_____

miniLAB 14
The Density of Carbon Dioxide

Hypothesizing Air is a mixture of mostly nitrogen and oxygen. Use observations to form a hypothesis about which has greater density, air or carbon dioxide.

Materials masking tape, aluminum foil, metric ruler, 1-L beaker, candle, matches, thermometer, barometer or weather radio, baking soda ($NaHCO_3$), vinegar (5% CH_3COOH)

Procedure

1. Record the temperature and the barometric pressure of the air in the classroom.
2. Roll a 23-cm × 30-cm piece of aluminum foil into a cylinder that is 6 cm × 30 cm. Tape the edges with masking tape.
3. Use matches to light a candle. **CAUTION:** *Run water over the extinguished match before throwing it away. Keep all hair and loose clothing away from the flame.*
4. Place 30 g of baking soda in the bottom of a large beaker. Add 40 mL of vinegar.
5. Quickly position the foil cylinder at approximately 45° up and away from the top of the candle flame.
6. While the reaction in the beaker is actively producing CO_2 gas, carefully pour the gas, but not the liquid, out of the beaker and into the top of the foil tube. Record your observations.

Analysis

1. Based on your observations, state a hypothesis about whether CO_2 is heavier or lighter than air.

   _____

2. Use the combined gas law to calculate molar volume at room temperature and atmospheric pressure.

   _____

3. Carbon dioxide gas (CO_2) has a molar mass of 44 g/mol. The two major components of air, which are oxygen and nitrogen, have molar masses of 32 g/mol and 28 g/mol, respectively. Calculate the room-temperature densities in g/L of nitrogen (N_2), oxygen (O_2), and carbon dioxide (CO_2) gases.

   _____

   _____

   _____

4. Do these calculations confirm your hypothesis? Explain.

   _____

   _____

   _____

Name _____   Date _____   Class _____

CHEMLAB 14

Using the Ideal Gas Law

The ideal gas law is a powerful tool that the chemist—and now you—can use to determine the molar mass of an unknown gas. By measuring the temperature, pressure, volume, and mass of a gas sample, you can calculate the molar mass of the gas.

Problem
How can the equation for the ideal gas law be used to calculate the molar mass of a gas?

Objectives
- **Measure** the mass, volume, temperature, and pressure of an insoluble gas collected over water.
- **Calculate** the molar mass of an unknown gas using the ideal gas equation.

Materials
aerosol can of duster
600-mL graduated beaker
bucket or bowl
thermometer (°C)
barometer or weather radio

plastic microtip pipette
latex tubing
glass tubing
scissors
electrical or duct tape
balance

Safety Precautions

- **Read and observe all cautions listed on the aerosol can of office equipment duster.**
- **Do not have any open flames in the room.**

Pre-Lab

1. Read the entire **CHEMLAB**.

2. Prepare all written materials that you will take into the laboratory. Be sure to include safety precautions and procedure notes. Use the data table on the next page.

3. Because you will collect the aerosol gas over water, the beaker contains both the aerosol gas and water vapor. Form a hypothesis about how the presence of water vapor will affect the calculated value of the molar mass of the gas. Explain.

_____

_____

_____

_____

_____

_____

_____

4. The following gases are or have been used in aerosol cans, some as propellants. Use the gases' molecular formulas to calculate their molar masses.

   a. propane, C_3H_8

   _____

   b. butane, C_4H_{10}

   _____

   c. dichlorodifluoromethane, CCl_2F_2

   _____

   d. tetrafluoroethane, $C_2H_2F_4$

   _____

5. Given the following data for a gas, use the equation for the ideal gas law to calculate the molar mass.

   a. mass = 0.810 g

   b. pressure = 0.954 atm

   c. volume = 0.461 L

   d. temperature = 291 K

Copyright © Glencoe/McGraw-Hill, a division of the McGraw-Hill Companies, Inc.

CHEMLAB (14)

Procedure

1. Place the bucket in the sink and fill it with water.

2. Submerge the beaker in the water. Then, invert it in the bucket, being careful to keep it completely filled with water.

3. Measure the mass of an aerosol can of office equipment duster. Record the mass in the data table.

4. Use scissors to cut the stem from a plastic microtip pipette.

5. Fit the pipette stem over the long plastic spray tip that comes with the aerosol can to extend the length of the tip and enlarge the diameter.

6. Connect one end of 30 cm of latex tubing to glass tubing that is 8 cm long.

7. Connect the other end to the pipette stem that is attached to the aerosol can. If necessary, tape any connections so that they don't leak.

8. Place the end of the glass tubing under the pour spout of the inverted beaker.

9. Hold the beaker down while you slowly release the gas from the aerosol can. Collect between 400 and 500 mL of the gas by water displacement.

10. To equalize the air pressure, lift the beaker so that the water level inside and outside the beaker is the same.

11. Carefully read the volume of the gas collected using the graduations on the beaker.

12. Record this volume of the gas collected in the data table.

13. Remove the tubing from the aerosol can.

14. Measure the mass of the can and record it in the data table.

15. Using a barometer or weather radio, record the atmospheric pressure in the data table.

16. Using a thermometer, determine air temperature. Record it in the data table.

Data and Calculations	
Mass of can before release of gas (g)	
Mass of can after release of gas (g)	
Mass of gas released (g)	
Air temperature (°C)	
Air temperature (K)	
Air pressure (list what unit was used)	
Air pressure (atm)	
Volume of gas collected (L)	

Cleanup and Disposal

1. Dispose of the empty can according to the instructions on its label.

2. Pour the water down the drain.

3. Discard any tape and the pipettes in the trash can.

4. Return all lab equipment to its proper place.

CHEMLAB 14

Analyze and Conclude

1. Using Numbers Fill in the remainder of the data table by calculating the mass of the gas that was released from the aerosol can, converting the atmospheric pressure from the units measured into atmospheres, and converting the air temperature into kelvins. Substitute your data from the table into the form of the ideal gas equation that solves for M. Calculate the molar mass of the gas in the can using the appropriate value for R.

2. Using Numbers Read the contents of the can and determine which of the gases from step 4 in the Pre-Lab is the most likely propellant.

_____

_____

3. Error Analysis Remember that you are collecting the gas after it has bubbled through water. What might happen to some of the gas as it goes through the water? What might be present in the gas in the beaker in addition to the gas from the can? Calculate the percent error using your calculated molar mass compared to the molar mass of the gas in the aerosol can.

_____

_____

_____

4. Interpreting Data Were your data consistent with the ideal gas law? Evaluate the pressure and temperature at which your experiment was done, and the polarity of the gas. Would you expect the gas in your experiment to behave as an ideal gas or a real gas?

_____

Real-World Chemistry

1. Explain why the label on an aerosol can warns against exposing the can to high heat.

_____

_____

2. Use the ideal gas law to explain why the wind blows.

_____

_____

_____

miniLAB 15

Freezing Point Depression

Measuring The colligative property of freezing point depression can be observed in a simple laboratory investigation. You will measure the temperatures of two beakers and their contents.

Materials 400-mL beakers (2), crushed ice, rock salt (NaCl), water, stirring rods (2), graduated cylinder, thermometers (2), balance

Procedure

1. Fill two 400-mL beakers with crushed ice. Add 50 mL of cold tap water to each beaker.
2. Stir the contents of each beaker with a stirring rod until both beakers are at a constant temperature, approximately 1 minute.
3. Measure the temperature of each beaker using a thermometer and record the readings.
4. Add 75 g of rock salt to one of the beakers. Continue stirring both beakers. Some of the salt will dissolve.
5. When the temperature in each beaker is constant, record the readings.
6. To clean up, flush the contents of each beaker down the drain with excess water.

Analysis

1. Compare your readings taken for the ice water and the salt water. How do you explain the observed temperature change?

_____

_____

_____

2. Why was salt only added to one of the beakers?

_____

3. Salt is a strong electrolyte that produces two ions, Na^+ and Cl^-, when it dissociates in water. Why is this important to consider when calculating the colligative property of freezing point depression?

_____

_____

_____

_____

4. Predict if it would be better to use coarse rock salt or fine table salt when making homemade ice cream. Explain.

_____

_____

CHEMLAB 15

Beer's Law

Finding the concentration of an unknown solution is an important procedure in laboratory work. One method commonly used to determine solution concentration is to measure how much of a single wavelength of light is absorbed by the solution and compare it to known values of concentration and wavelength. Light absorbance is directly related to the concentration of a solution. This relationship is called Beer's law.

Problem
How is light absorbance used to find the concentration of a blue dye solution?

Objectives
- **Prepare** solutions of known concentration from a blue dye stock solution.
- **Measure** the absorbance of known and unknown aqueous solutions.
- **Infer** the relationship between light absorbance and concentration of a solution.

Materials
CBL system
graphing calculator
Vernier colorimeter
DIN adapter and
  cable
TI GRAPH LINK
  (optional)
cuvette
cotton swabs
tissues for wiping
  cuvette

blue dye stock
  solution
unknown solution
distilled water
50-mL graduated
  cylinder
100-mL beaker (2)
small test tube (5)
test-tube rack
pipette (2)
pipette bulb
stirring rod

Safety Precautions

- **Always wear safety goggles and a lab apron.**
- **The food-coloring solution can stain clothes.**

Pre-Lab

1. Read the entire **CHEMLAB** procedure.

2. What is the total volume of solution in each test tube? Calculate the percent by volume of the solutions in test tubes 1 through 5. Use the data table on the next page.

_____

_____

_____

3. Review with your teacher how a colorimeter works. How are absorbance (*A*) and transmittance (%*T*) related?

_____

4. What is occurring during step 3 of the procedure? Why is a cuvette of water used?

_____

_____

_____

_____

CHEMLAB (15)

Procedure

1. Transfer 30 mL of blue dye stock solution into a beaker. Transfer 30 mL of distilled water into another beaker.

2. Label five clean, dry test tubes 1 through 5.

3. Pipette 2 mL of blue dye stock solution from the beaker into test tube 1, 4 mL into test tube 2, 6 mL into test tube 3, and 8 mL into test tube 4. **CAUTION:** *Always pipette using a pipette bulb.*

4. With another pipette, transfer 8 mL of distilled water from the beaker into test tube 1, 6 mL into tube 2, 4 mL into tube 3, and 2 mL into tube 4.

5. Mix the solution in test tube 1 with a stirring rod. Rinse and dry the stirring rod. Repeat this procedure with each test tube.

6. Pipette 10 mL of blue dye stock into test tube 5.

7. Load the ChemBio program into the calculator. Connect the CBL to the colorimeter using a DIN adapter. Connect the CBL to the calculator using a link cable. Begin the ChemBio program on the calculator. Select "1" probe. Select 4: COLORIMETER. Enter Channel "1."

8. Fill a cuvette about three-fourths full with distilled water and dry its outside with a tissue. To calibrate the colorimeter, place the cuvette in the colorimeter and close the lid. Turn the wavelength knob to 0%T. Press TRIGGER on the CBL and enter 0 into the calculator. Turn the wavelength knob to Red (635 nm). Press TRIGGER on the CBL and enter 100 into the calculator. Leave the colorimeter set on Red for the rest of the lab. Remove the cuvette from the colorimeter. Empty the distilled water from the cuvette. Dry the inside of the cuvette with a clean cotton swab.

9. Select COLLECT DATA from the MAIN MENU. Select TRIGGER/PROMPT from the DATA COLLECTION menu. Fill the cuvette about three-fourths full with the solution from test tube 1. Dry the outside of the cuvette with a tissue and place the cuvette in the colorimeter. Close the lid. After 10 to 15 seconds, press TRIGGER and enter the concentration in percent from your data table into the calculator.

Known and Unknown Solutions Data			
Test tube	Concentration (%)	%T	A
1			
2			
3			
4			
5			
Unknown			

Remove the cuvette and pour out the solution. Rinse the inside of the cuvette with distilled water and dry it with a clean cotton swab. Repeat this step for test tubes 2 through 5.

10. Select STOP AND GRAPH from the DATA COLLECTION menu when you have finished with data collection. Draw the graph, or use the TI Graph-Link to make a copy of the graph from the calculator screen. You also will want to copy the data from the STAT list into your data table (or you can print it from a screen print using Graph-Link).

11. Clean the cuvette with a cotton swab and fill it about three-fourths full with the unknown dye solution. Place the cuvette in the colorimeter and close the lid. From the MAIN MENU, select COLLECT DATA (do not select SET UP PROBES as this will erase your data lists). Select MONITOR INPUT from the DATA COLLECTION MENU. Press ENTER to monitor the absorbance value of the colorimeter. After about 10–15 seconds, record the absorbance value and record it in your data table.

Cleanup and Disposal

1. All of the blue dye solutions can be rinsed down the drain.

2. Turn off the colorimeter. Clean and dry the cuvette. Return all equipment to its proper place.

CHEMLAB 15

Analyze and Conclude

1. **Analyzing Data** Evaluate how close your graph is to the direct relationship exhibited by Beer's law by doing a linear-regression line. Select FIT CURVE from the MAIN MENU (do not select SET UP PROBES as this will erase your data lists). Select LINEAR L1,L2. The calculator will give you an equation in the form of $y = ax + b$. One indicator of the fit of your graph is the size of b. A small value of b means the graph passes close to the origin. The closer the correlation coefficient r reported by the program is to 1.00, the better the fit of the graph.

_____

_____

2. **Drawing Conclusions** Use the graph of your absorbance and concentration data to determine the concentration of your unknown solution.

_____

_____

3. **Form a Hypothesis** Would you obtain the same data if red dye was used? Explain.

_____

_____

_____

4. **Error Analysis** Analyze your b and r values. How closely do your results match Beer's law? Reexamine the procedure and suggest reasons why the correlation coefficient from your data does not equal 1.00.

_____

_____

_____

Real-World Chemistry

1. Explain how Beer's law can be applied in food, drug, and medical testing.

_____

_____

2. The reaction of alcohol with orange dichromate ions to produce blue-green chromium(III) ions is used in the Breathalyzer test, a test that measures the presence of alcohol in a person's breath. How could a colorimeter be used in this analysis?

_____

_____

miniLAB 16

Enthalpy of Fusion for Ice

Applying Concepts When ice is added to water at room temperature, the water provides the energy for two processes. The first process is the melting of the ice. The energy required to melt ice is the enthalpy of fusion (ΔH_{fus}). The second process is raising the temperature of the melted ice from its initial temperature of 0.0°C to the final temperature of the liquid water. In this experiment, you will collect data to calculate the enthalpy of fusion for ice.

Materials foam cup, thermometer, stirring rod, ice, water, balance

Procedure

1. Measure the mass of an empty foam cup and record it in your data table.
2. Fill the foam cup about one-third full of water. Measure and record the mass.
3. Place the thermometer in the cup. Read and record the initial temperature of the water.
4. Quickly place a small quantity of ice in the foam cup. Gently stir the water with a stirring rod until the ice melts. Record the lowest temperature reached as the final temperature.
5. Measure the mass of the cup and water.

Analysis

1. The heat lost by the liquid water equals the heat needed to melt the ice plus the heat needed to increase the temperature of the melted ice from 0.0°C to the final temperature. Calculate the heat lost by the water.

_____

2. Calculate the heat gained by the melted ice as its temperature rose from 0.0°C to the final temperature.

_____

3. The difference between the heat lost by the water and the heat gained by the melted ice equals the heat of fusion. Calculate the heat of fusion in joules per gram of ice.

_____

4. Calculate ΔH_{fus} in kJ/mol.

_____

5. Calculate the percent error of your experimental ΔH_{fus}. Compare your value to the actual value 6.01 kJ/mol.

_____

Copyright © Glencoe/McGraw-Hill, a division of the McGraw-Hill Companies, Inc.

CHEMLAB 16

Calorimetry

In this laboratory investigation, you will use the methods of calorimetry to approximate the amount of energy contained in a potato chip. The burning of a potato chip releases heat stored in the substances contained in the chip. The heat will be absorbed by a mass of water.

Problem

How many Calories of energy does the potato chip contain? How can the experiment be improved to provide a more accurate answer?

Objectives

- **Identify** the reactants and products in the reaction.
- **Measure** mass and temperature in order to calculate the amount of heat released in the reaction.
- **Propose** changes in the procedure and design of the equipment to decrease the percent error.

Materials

large potato chip
250-mL beaker
100-mL graduated
  cylinder
evaporating dish
thermometer
ring stand with ring
wire gauze
matches
stirring rod
balance

Safety Precautions

- **Always wear safety goggles and a lab apron.**
- **Tie back long hair.**
- **Hot objects may not appear to be hot.**
- **Do not heat broken, chipped, or cracked glassware.**
- **Do not eat any items used in the lab.**

Pre-Lab

1. Read the entire **CHEMLAB.**

2. Prepare all written materials that you will take into the laboratory. Be sure to include safety precautions and procedure notes. Use the data table on the next page.

3. Form a hypothesis about how the quantity of heat produced by the combustion reaction will compare with the quantity of heat absorbed by the water.

_____

_____

_____

4. What formula will you use to calculate the quantity of heat absorbed by the water?

_____

5. Assuming that the potato chip contains compounds made up of carbon and hydrogen, what gases will be produced in the combustion reaction?

_____

CHEMLAB 16

Procedure

1. Measure the mass of a potato chip and record it in the data table.

2. Place the potato chip in an evaporating dish on the metal base of the ring stand. Position the ring and wire gauze so that they will be 10 cm above the top of the potato chip.

3. Measure the mass of an empty 250-mL beaker and record it in the data table.

4. Using the graduated cylinder, measure 50 mL of water and pour it into the beaker. Measure the mass of the beaker and water and record it in the data table.

5. Place the beaker on the wire gauze on the ring stand.

6. Measure and record the initial temperature of the water.

7. Use a match to ignite the bottom of the potato chip.

8. With a stirring rod, stir the water in the beaker while the chip burns. Measure the highest temperature of the water and record it in the data table.

Observations of the Burning of a Potato Chip	
Mass of beaker and 50 mL of water	
Mass of empty beaker	
Mass of water in beaker	
Mass of potato chip	
Highest temperature of water	
Initial temperature of water	
Change in temperature	

Cleanup and Disposal

1. Clean all lab equipment and return it to its proper place.

2. Wash your hands thoroughly after all lab work and cleanup is complete.

Analyze and Conclude

1. **Classifying** Is the reaction exothermic or endothermic? Explain how you know.

_____

_____

2. **Observing and Inferring** Describe the reactant and products of the chemical reaction. Was the reactant (potato chip) completely consumed? What evidence supports your answer?

_____

_____

_____

3. **Using Numbers** Calculate the mass of water in the beaker and the temperature change of the water. Use $q = c \times m \times \Delta T$ to calculate how much heat in joules was transferred to the water in the beaker by the burning of one chip.

_____

_____

CHEMLAB 16

4. Using Numbers Convert the quantity of heat in joules/chip to Calories/chip.

_____

_____

5. Using Numbers From the information on the chip's container, determine the mass in grams of one serving. Using your data, calculate the number of Calories that would be released by the combustion of one serving of chips.

_____

_____

6. Error Analysis Use the chip's container to determine how many Calories are contained in one serving. Compare your calculated Calories per serving with the value on the chip's container. Calculate the percent error.

_____

_____

7. Observing and Inferring Was all of the heat that was released collected by the water in the beaker? How can the experimental equipment be improved to decrease the percent error?

_____

_____

_____

Real-World Chemistry

1. From the ingredients identified on the potato chip container, list the actual substances that burned to produce energy. Are there any ingredients that did not produce energy? Explain.

_____

_____

_____

2. You have discovered that potato chips provide a significant number of Calories per serving. Would it be advisable to make potato chips a substantial part of your diet? Explain.

_____

_____

_____

Copyright © Glencoe/McGraw-Hill, a division of the McGraw-Hill Companies, Inc.

miniLAB 17

Examining Reaction Rate and Temperature

Recognizing Cause and Effect Several factors affect the rate of a chemical reaction. This lab allows you to examine the effect of temperature on a common chemical reaction.

Materials small beaker, thermometer, hot plate, 250-mL beaker, balance, water, effervescent (bicarbonate) tablet, stopwatch or clock with second hand

Procedure

1. Take a single effervescent tablet and break it into four roughly equal pieces.
2. Measure the mass of one piece of the tablet. Measure 50 mL of room-temperature water (approximately 20°C) into a small cup or beaker. Measure the temperature of the water.
3. With a stopwatch ready, add the piece of tablet to the water. Record the amount of time elapsed between when the tablet hits the water and when you see that all of the piece of tablet has dissolved in the water.
4. Repeat steps 2 and 3 twice more, except use water temperatures of about 50°C and 65°C. Be sure to raise the temperature gradually and maintain the desired temperature (equilibrate) throughout the run.

Analysis

1. Calculate the reaction rate by finding the mass/time for each run. Use the data table below.
2. Graph the reaction rate (mass/time) versus temperature for the runs in the space below.
3. What is the relationship between reaction rate and temperature for this reaction?

_____

4. Using your graphed data, predict the reaction rate for the reaction carried out at 40°C. Heat and equilibrate the water to 40°C and use the last piece of tablet to test your prediction.

_____

5. How did your prediction for the reaction rate at 40°C compare to the actual reaction rate?

_____

Data Table			
Mass of Tablet (g)	Reaction time (s)	Reaction rate (g/s)	Temperature (°C)

CHEMLAB 17

Concentration and Reaction Rate

The collision theory describes how the change in concentration of one reactant affects the rate of chemical reactions. In this laboratory experiment, you will observe how concentration affects the reaction rate.

Problem
How does the concentration of a reactant affect the reaction rate?

Objectives
- **Sequence** the acid concentrations from the most to the least concentrated.
- **Observe** which concentration results in the fastest reaction rate.

Materials
10-mL graduated pipette
safety pipette filler
6M hydrochloric acid
distilled water
25 mm × 150 mm test tubes (4)
test-tube rack
magnesium ribbon
emery cloth or fine sandpaper
scissors
plastic ruler
tongs
watch with second hand
stirring rod

Safety Precautions

- **Always wear safety goggles and a lab apron.**
- **Never pipette any chemical by mouth.**
- **Do not have any open flames in the room.**

Pre-Lab

1. Read the entire **CHEMLAB.** Prepare all written materials that you will take into the laboratory. Be sure to include safety precautions and procedure notes. Use the data table on the next page.

2. Use emery paper or sandpaper to polish the magnesium ribbon until it is shiny. Use scissors to cut the magnesium into four 1-cm pieces.

3. Place the four test tubes in the test-tube rack. Label the test tubes #1 (6.0M HCl), #2 (3M HCl), #3 (1.5M HCl), and #4 (0.75M HCl).

4. Form a hypothesis about how the chemical reaction rate is related to reactant concentration.

_____

_____

_____

5. What reactant quantity is held constant? What are the independent and dependent variables?

_____

_____

_____

6. What gas is produced in the reaction between magnesium and hydrochloric acid? Write the balanced formula equation for the reaction.

_____

_____

_____

Copyright © Glencoe/McGraw-Hill, a division of the McGraw-Hill Companies, Inc.

CHEMLAB 17

7. Why is it important to clean the magnesium ribbon? If one of the four pieces is not thoroughly polished, how will the rate of the reaction involving that piece be affected?

_____

_____

_____

_____

_____

Procedure

1. Use a safety pipette filler to draw 10 mL of 6.0M hydrochloric acid (HCl) into a 10-mL graduated pipette.

2. Dispense the 10 mL of 6.0M HCl into test tube #1.

3. Draw 5.0 mL of the 6.0M HCl from test tube #1 with the empty pipette. Dispense this acid into test tube #2 and use the pipette to add an additional 5.0 mL of distilled water to the acid. Use the stirring rod to mix thoroughly. This solution is 3.0M HCl.

4. Draw 5.0 mL of the 3.0M HCl from test tube #2 with the empty pipette. Dispense this acid into test tube #3 and use the pipette to add an additional 5.0 mL of distilled water to the acid. Use the stirring rod to mix thoroughly. This solution is 1.5M HCl.

5. Draw 5.0 mL of the 1.5M HCl from test tube #3 with the empty pipette. Dispense this acid into

test tube #4 and use the pipette to add an additional 5.0 mL of distilled water to the acid. Use the stirring rod to mix thoroughly. This solution is 0.75M HCl.

6. Draw 5.0 mL of the 0.75M HCl from test tube #4 with the empty pipette. Neutralize and discard it in the sink.

7. Using the tongs, place a 1-cm length of magnesium ribbon into test tube #1. Record the time in seconds that it takes for the bubbling to stop.

8. Repeat step 7 using the remaining three test tubes of HCl and the three remaining pieces of magnesium ribbon. Record in the data table the time (in seconds) it takes for the bubbling to stop.

Reaction Time Data		
Test tube	[HCl] (*M*)	Time (s)
1		
2		
3		
4		

Cleanup and Disposal

1. Place acid solutions in an acid discard container. Your teacher will neutralize the acid for proper disposal.

2. Wash thoroughly all test tubes and lab equipment.

3. Discard other materials as directed by your teacher.

4. Return all lab equipment to its proper place.

Analyze and Conclude

1. **Analyzing** In step 6, why is 5.0 mL HCl discarded?

_____

2. **Making and Using Graphs** Plot the concentration of the acid on the *x*-axis and time it takes for the bubbling to stop on the *y*-axis. Draw a smooth curve through the data points.

3. Interpreting Graphs Is the curve in question 2 linear or nonlinear? What does the slope tell you?

_____

4. Drawing a Conclusion Based on your graph, what do you conclude about the relationship between the acid concentration and the reaction rate?

_____

_____

5. Hypothesizing Write a hypothesis using the collision theory, reaction rate, and reactant concentration to explain your results.

_____

_____

_____

_____

6. Designing an Experiment Write a brief statement of how you would set up an experiment to test your hypothesis.

_____

_____

_____

7. Error Analysis Compare your experimental results with those of several other students in the laboratory. Explain the differences.

_____

_____

_____

Real-World Chemistry

1. Describe a situation that may occur in your daily life that exemplifies the effect of concentration on the rate of a reaction.

_____

_____

_____

2. Some hair-care products, such as hot-oil treatments, must be heated before application. Explain in terms of factors affecting reaction rates why heat is required.

_____

_____

_____

miniLAB 18

Shifts in Equilibrium

Observing and Inferring Le Châtelier's principle states that if a stress is placed on a reaction at equilibrium, the system will shift in a way that will relieve the stress. In this experiment, you will witness an equilibrium shift in a colorful way.

Materials test tubes (2); 10-mL graduated cylinder; 250-mL beaker; concentrated hydrochloric acid; 0.1M $CoCl_2$ solution; ice bath; table salt; hot plate

Procedures

1. Place about 2 mL of 0.1M $CoCl_2$ solution in a test tube. Record the color of the solution.

2. Add about 3 mL of concentrated HCl to the test tube. Record the color of the solution. **CAUTION:** *HCl can burn skin and clothing.*

3. Add enough water to the test tube to make a color change occur. Record the color.

4. Add about 2 mL of 0.1M $CoCl_2$ to another test tube. Add concentrated HCl dropwise until the solution turns purple. If the solution becomes blue, add water until it turns purple.

5. Place the test tube in an ice bath that has had some salt sprinkled into the ice water. Record the color of the solution in the test tube.

6. Place the test tube in a hot water bath that is at least 70°C. Record the color of the solution.

Analysis

1. The equation for the reversible reaction in this experiment is

   $$Co(H_2O)_6^{2+} + 4Cl^- \rightleftharpoons CoCl_4^{2-} + 6H_2O$$
        pink   blue

   Use the equation to explain your observations of color in steps 1–3.

   _____

   _____

2. Explain how the equilibrium shifts when energy is added or removed.

   _____

   _____

CHEMLAB 18

Comparing Two Solubility Product Constants

L e Châtelier's principle is a powerful tool for explaining how a reaction at equilibrium shifts when a stress is placed on the system. In this experiment, you can use Le Châtelier's principle to evaluate the relative solubilities of two precipitates. By observing the formation of two precipitates in the same system, you can infer the relationship between the solubilities of the two ionic compounds and the numerical values of their solubility product constants (K_{sp}). You will be able to verify your own experimental results by calculating the molar solubilities of the two compounds using the K_{sp} for each compound.

Problem

How can a saturated solution of one ionic compound react with another ionic compound to form another precipitate? What is the relationship between solubility and the K_{sp} value of a saturated solution?

Objectives

- **Observe** evidence that a precipitate is in equilibrium with its ions in solution.
- **Infer** the relative solubilities of two sparingly soluble ionic compounds.
- **Compare** the values of the K_{sp} for two different compounds and relate them to your observations.
- **Explain** your observations of the two precipitates by using Le Châtelier's principle.
- **Calculate** the molar solubilities of the two ionic compounds from their K_{sp} values.

Materials

$AgNO_3$ solution
NaCl solution
Na_2S solution
24-well microplate
thin-stem
 pipettes (3)
wash bottle

Safety Precautions

- **Always wear safety goggles, gloves, and a lab apron.**
- **Silver nitrate is highly toxic and will stain skin and clothing.**

Pre-Lab

1. Read the entire **CHEMLAB.**

2. Prepare all written materials that you will take into the laboratory. Be sure to include safety precautions and procedure notes. Use the data table on the next page.

3. State Le Châtelier's principle.

_____

_____

_____

_____

4. Identify the control and the independent variable in the experiment.

_____

_____

5. When a solid dissolves to form two ions and the solid's K_{sp} is known, what is the mathematical formula you can use to calculate the molar solubility?

_____

_____

_____

Copyright © Glencoe/McGraw-Hill, a division of the McGraw-Hill Companies, Inc.

CHEMLAB ⑱

Procedure

1. Place 10 drops of $AgNO_3$ solution in well A1 of a 24-well microplate. Place 10 drops of the same solution in well A2.

2. Add 10 drops of NaCl solution to well A1 and 10 drops to well A2.

3. Allow the precipitate to form in each well. Record your observations.

4. To well A2, add 10 drops of Na_2S solution.

5. Allow the precipitate to form. Record your observations of the precipitate.

6. Compare the contents of wells A1 and A2 and record your observations in the data table.

Cleanup and Disposal

1. Use a wash bottle to transfer the contents of the well plate into a large waste beaker.

2. Wash your hands thoroughly after all lab work and cleanup are complete.

Precipitate Formation	
	Observations
Step 3	
Step 5	
Step 6	

Analyze and Conclude

1. **Analyzing Information** Write the complete equation for the double-replacement reaction that occurred when NaCl and $AgNO_3$ were mixed in wells A1 and A2 in step 2. Write the net ionic equation.

   _____

   _____

2. **Analyzing Information** Write the solubility product constant expression for the equilibrium established in wells A1 and A2 in step 2. K_{sp} (AgCl) $= 1.8 \times 10^{-10}$.

   _____

3. **Analyzing Information** Write the equation for the equilibrium that was established in well A2 when you added Na_2S. K_{sp} (Ag_2S) $= 8 \times 10^{-48}$

   _____

4. **Inferring** Identify the two precipitates by color. _____

5. **Comparing and Contrasting** Compare the K_{sp} values for the two precipitates. Infer which of the two ionic compounds is more soluble.

   _____

6. **Recognizing Cause and Effect** Use Le Châtelier's principle to explain how the addition of Na_2S in procedure step 4 affected the equilibrium established in well A2.

   _____

   _____

   _____

CHEMLAB 18

7. **Using Numbers** Calculate the molar solubilities of the two precipitates using the K_{sp} values. Which of the precipitates is more soluble?

_____

_____

8. **Thinking Critically** What evidence from this experiment supports your answer to question 7? Explain.

_____

9. **Error Analysis** Did you observe the well plate from the side as well as from the top? What did you notice?

_____

10. **Developing General Rules** The solubility of an ionic compound depends upon the nature of the cations and anions that make up the compound. The reactants you used in this **CHEMLAB** are all soluble ionic compounds, whereas the precipitates are insoluble. How does soluble Na_2S differ from insoluble Ag_2S? How does soluble NaCl differ from insoluble AgCl? Use this information and K_{sp} data from **Table 18-3** and the *Handbook of Chemistry and Physics* to develop general rules for solubility. What group of metal ions is not found in sparingly soluble compounds? What polyatomic ions, positive and negative, form only soluble ionic compounds? How does K_{sp} relate to a compound's relative solubility?

_____

Real-World Chemistry

1. Research how industries use precipitation to remove hazardous chemicals from waste-water before returning it to the water cycle.

_____

_____

_____

2. *Hard water* is the name given to water supplies that contain significant concentrations of Mg^{2+} and Ca^{2+} ions. Check on the solubility of ionic compounds formed with these ions and predict what problems they may cause.

_____

_____

3. Explain what would happen if you lost the stopper for a bottle of a saturated solution of lead sulfate ($PbSO_4$) and the bottle stood open to the air for a week. Would your answer be different if it was an unsaturated solution? Explain.

_____

_____

miniLAB 19
Acid Strength

Observing and Inferring The electrical conductivities of solutions of weak acids, such as acetic acid, are related to the degree of ionization of the acid.

Materials glacial acetic acid; distilled water; 10-mL graduated cylinder; dropping pipette; 50-mL beaker; 24-well microplate; conductivity tester with battery; stirring rod

Procedure

1. Use a 10-mL graduated cylinder to measure 3 mL of glacial acetic acid. Use a dropping pipette to transfer the 3 mL of glacial acetic acid into well A1 of a 24-well microplate.

2. Lower the electrodes of a conductivity tester into the glacial acetic acid in well A1. Record your results.

3. Rinse the graduated cylinder with water. Prepare a 6.0*M* solution of acetic acid by adding 3.4 mL of glacial acetic acid to 6.6 mL of distilled water in the 10-mL graduated cylinder.

4. Empty the 10 mL of diluted acid into a 50-mL beaker. After mixing, transfer 3 mL of the 6.0*M* acetic acid into well A2. Save the remaining 6.0*M* acetic acid for procedure step 5. Test and record the conductivity of the solution.

5. Prepare a 1.0*M* acetic acid solution by adding 1.7 mL of 6.0*M* acetic acid to 8.3 mL of distilled water in the 10-mL graduated cylinder. Empty the 10 mL of diluted acid into the rinsed 50-mL beaker. After mixing, transfer 3 mL of the 1.0*M* acetic acid into well A3. Save the remaining 1.0*M* acetic acid for procedure step 6. Test and record the conductivity of the solution.

6. Prepare a 0.1*M* acetic acid solution by adding 1.0 mL of 1.0*M* acetic acid to 9.0 mL of distilled water in the rinsed 10-mL graduated cylinder. Empty the 10 mL of diluted acid into the rinsed 50-mL beaker. After mixing, transfer 3 mL of the 0.1*M* acetic acid into well A4. Test and record the conductivity of the solution.

Analysis

1. Write the equation for the ionization of acetic acid in water and the equilibrium constant expression. ($K_{eq} = 1.8 \times 10^{-5}$) What does the size of K_{eq} indicate about the degree of ionization of acetic acid?

2. Do the following approximate percents ionization fit your laboratory results: glacial acetic acid, 0.1%; 6.0*M* acetic acid, 0.2%; 1.0*M* acetic acid, 0.4%; 0.1*M* acetic acid, 1.3%? Explain.

3. State a hypothesis that will explain your observations and incorporate your answer to Question 2.

4. Based on your hypothesis, what can you conclude about the need to use large amounts of water for rinsing when acid spills on living tissue?

CHEMLAB 19

Standardizing a Base Solution by Titration

The procedure called titration can be used to standardize a solution of a base, which means determine its molar concentration. To standardize a base, a solution of the base with unknown molarity is gradually added to a solution containing a known mass of an acid. The procedure enables you to determine when the number of moles of added OH^- ions from the base equals the number of moles of H^+ ion from the acid.

Problem

How can you determine the molar concentration of a base solution? How do you know when the neutralization reaction has reached the equivalence point?

Objectives

- **Recognize** the color change of the indicator that shows that the equivalence point has been reached.
- **Measure** the mass of the acid and the volume of the base solution used.
- **Calculate** the molar concentration of the base solution.

Materials

50-mL burette
burette clamp
ring stand
sodium hydroxide
  pellets (NaOH)
potassium hydro-
  gen phthalate
  ($KHC_8H_4O_4$)
distilled water
weighing bottle
spatula

250-mL Erlenmeyer
  flask
500-mL Florence
  flask and rubber
  stopper
250-mL beaker
centigram balance
wash bottle
phenolphthalein
  solution
dropper

Safety Precautions

- **Always wear safety goggles and a lab apron.**

Pre-Lab

1. What is the equivalence point of a titration?

_____

_____

_____

2. Read the entire **CHEMLAB.**

3. What is the independent variable? The dependent variable? Constant?

_____

_____

_____

4. When the solid acid dissolves to form ions, how many moles of H^+ ions are produced for every mole of acid used?

_____

_____

5. What is the formula used to calculate molarity?

_____

_____

_____

6. Prepare a data table that will accommodate multiple titration trials.

7. List safety precautions that must be taken.

_____

CHEMLAB 19

Procedure

1. Place approximately 4 g NaOH in a 500-mL Florence flask. Add enough water to dissolve the pellets and bring the volume of the NaOH solution to about 400 mL. **CAUTION:** *The solution will get hot.* Keep the stopper in the flask.

2. Use the weighing bottle to mass by difference about 0.40 g of potassium hydrogen phthalate (molar mass = 204.32 g/mol) into a 250-mL Erlenmeyer flask. Record this data.

3. Using a wash bottle, rinse down the insides of the flask and add enough water to make about 50 mL of solution. Add 2 drops of phenolphthalein indicator solution.

4. Set up the burette as shown. Rinse the burette with about 10 mL of your base solution. Discard the rinse solution in a discard beaker.

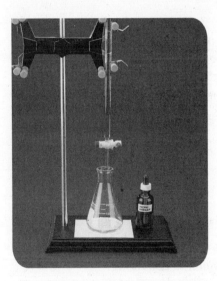

5. Fill the burette with NaOH solution. To remove any air trapped in the tip, allow a small amount of the base to flow from the tip of the burette into the discard beaker. Read the burette to the nearest 0.02 mL and record this initial reading. The meniscus of the solution in the burette should be at eye level when you make a reading.

6. Place a piece of white paper under the burette. Allow the NaOH solution to flow slowly from the burette into the flask containing the acid. Control the flow of the base solution with your left hand, and gently swirl the flask with your right hand.

7. The NaOH solution may be added in a rapid stream of drops until the pink color begins to last longer as the flask is swirled. At this stage, begin adding the base drop by drop.

8. The equivalence point is reached when one additional drop of base turns the acid in the flask pink. The pink color should persist as the flask is swirled. Record the final volume in the burette.

9. Calculate the molarity of your base using steps 2–5 on the next page.

10. Refill your burette with base. Rinse your Erlenmeyer flask with water. Repeat the titration with additional samples of acid until you get three trials that show close agreement between the calculated values of the molarity.

Cleanup and Disposal

1. The neutralized solutions can be washed down the sink using plenty of water.

Titration Data	
	Trial 1
mass of weighing bottle and acid	
mass of weighing bottle	
mass of solid acid	
moles of acid	
moles of base required	
final reading of base burette	
initial reading of base burette	
volume of base used in mL	
molarity of base	

CHEMLAB 19

Analyze and Conclude

1. Observing and Inferring Identify the characteristics of this neutralization reaction.

_____

2. Collecting and Interpreting Data Complete the data table. Calculate the number of moles of acid used in each trial by dividing the mass of the sample by the molar mass of the acid.

_____

_____

3. Using Numbers How many moles of base are required to react with the moles of acid you used?

_____

_____

4. Using Numbers Convert the volume of base used from milliliters to liters.

_____

5. Analyze and Conclude For each trial, calculate the molar concentration of the base by dividing the moles of base by the volume of base in liters.

_____

6. Error Analysis How well did your calculated molarities agree? Explain any irregularities.

_____

_____

Real-World Chemistry

1. Use what you have learned about titration to design a field investigation to determine whether your area is affected by acid rain. Research the factors that affect the pH of rain, such as location, prevailing winds, and industries. Form a hypothesis about the pH of rain in your area. What equipment will you need to collect samples? To perform the titration? What indicator will you use?

_____

_____

_____

_____

_____

_____

miniLAB 20
Cleaning by Redox

Applying Concepts The tarnish on silver is silver sulfide, which is formed when the silver reacts with sulfide compounds in the environment. In this miniLAB, you will use an oxidation–reduction reaction to remove the tarnish from silver or a silver-plated object.

Materials aluminum foil, steel wool, small tarnished silver object, 400-mL beaker (or size large enough to hold the tarnished object), baking soda, table salt, hot plate, beaker tongs

Procedure

1. Buff a piece of aluminum foil lightly with steel wool to remove any oxide coating.
2. Wrap the tarnished object in the aluminum foil, making sure that the tarnished area makes firm contact with the foil.
3. Place the wrapped object in the beaker and add sufficient tap water to cover.
4. Add about 1 spoonful of baking soda and about 1 spoonful of table salt.
5. Set the beaker and contents on a hot plate and heat until the water is nearly boiling. Maintain the heat approximately 15 min until the tarnish disappears.

Analysis

1. Write the equation for the reaction of silver with hydrogen sulfide, yielding silver sulfide and hydrogen.

   _____

2. Write the equation for the reaction of the tarnish (silver sulfide) with the aluminum foil, yielding aluminum sulfide and silver.

   _____

3. Which metal, aluminum or silver, is more reactive? How do you know this from your results?

   _____

   _____

4. Why should you not use an aluminum pan to clean silver objects by this method?

   _____

CHEMLAB 20

Redox Reactions

In Section 20.2, a redox reaction involving copper and nitric acid is discussed. This reaction is balanced by a method called the oxidation-number method. In this lab, you will carry out this reaction, along with another redox reaction that involves a common household substance. You will practice balancing various redox reactions using both the oxidation-number method (from Section 20.2) and the half-reaction method (from Section 20.3).

Problem

What are some examples of redox reactions and how can the equations describing them be balanced?

Objectives

- **Observe** various redox reactions.
- **Balance** redox reactions using the oxidation-number method.
- **Balance** redox reactions using the half-reaction method.

Materials

copper metal
6M nitric acid
evaporating dish
forceps
distilled water
dropper pipette
spoon
household ammonia
crystal drain cleaner
thermometer
250-mL beaker

Safety Precautions

- The reaction of copper with nitric acid should be done in a ventilation hood. Do not breathe the fumes from this reaction.
- Nitric acid and ammonia can cause burns. Avoid contact with skin and eyes.

Pre-Lab

1. Read the entire **CHEMLAB.**

2. Prepare all written materials that you will take into the laboratory. Be sure to include safety precautions and procedure notes. Use the data table on the next page.

3. Review what a redox reaction is.

_____

_____

4. Read the label of the crystal drain cleaner package. Understand that the compound is solid sodium hydroxide that contains aluminum. When the material is added to water, sodium hydroxide dissolves rapidly, producing heat. Aluminum reacts with water in the basic solution to produce $Al(OH)_4^-$ ions and hydrogen gas. Is aluminum oxidized or reduced in the reaction? Is hydrogen oxidized or reduced in the reaction? Explain your answers.

_____

_____

_____

_____

Copyright © Glencoe/McGraw-Hill, a division of the McGraw-Hill Companies, Inc.

CHEMLAB 20

Procedure

1. In a ventilation hood, place a piece of copper metal in a clean, dry evaporating dish. Add enough 6*M* nitric acid to cover the metal. **CAUTION:** *Nitric acid can cause burns. The reaction of nitric acid with copper generates dangerous fumes. Use a ventilation hood.* Observe what happens and record your observations in the data table.

2. Pour about 2 mL of the solution from the evaporating dish into a test tube that contains about 2 mL of distilled water. Add ammonia until a change occurs. Record your observation in the data table.

3. Add about 50 mL of tap water to a 250-mL beaker. Use a thermometer to measure the temperature of the water. Record your observations in the data table.

4. Pour approximately 1 cm³ of dry drain cleaner onto a watchglass. **CAUTION:** *Drain cleaner is*

caustic and will burn skin. Use forceps to move the crystals and observe their composition. Record your observations in the data table.

5. Carefully pour about one-half spoonful of the crystals into the water in the beaker. As the crystals react with the water, watch the thermometer in the water for a few minutes and record in the data table the highest temperature reached and any other observations you make.

Cleanup and Disposal

1. After step 1 is completed, use forceps to remove any excess pieces of copper metal. Rinse the copper metal with tap water and dispose of the metal as your teacher instructs.

2. After step 2 is finished, pour the solution down the drain and flush with a lot of water.

3. After step 5 is finished, pour the solution down the drain and flush with a lot of water.

Data Table	
Step 1	
Step 2	
Step 3	
Step 4	
Step 5	

Analyze and Conclude

1. **Applying Concepts** The reaction between copper and nitric acid is discussed in Section 20.2. Write the half-reaction for the substance that is oxidized.

_____

2. **Applying Concepts** Write the half-reaction for the substance that is reduced.

_____

3. **Thinking Critically** In step 2, a deep blue copper–ammonia complex is formed according to the following reaction.

$$Cu^{2+} + NH_3 \rightarrow Cu(NH_3)_4{}^{2+}$$

Is this a redox reaction? Why or why not?

_____

CHEMLAB (20)

4. Using Numbers The following side reaction occurs from the reaction of copper with nitric acid.

$$Cu + HNO_3 \rightarrow Cu(NO_3)_2 + NO + H_2O$$

Balance this redox reaction using both the oxidation-number method and the half-reaction method.

_____

5. Using Numbers Write and balance the redox reaction of sodium hydroxide with aluminum and water.

_____

6. Error Analysis Give possible reasons why you might not have been able to balance the equation for the redox reaction you performed in this experiment.

_____

_____

Real-World Chemistry

1. Using your observations in this lab, how do drain cleaning crystals remove clogs?

_____

_____

2. Ammonia and bleach are two common household chemicals that should never be mixed. One product of this reaction is chloramine, a poisonous, volatile compound. The reaction is as follows.

$$NH_3 + ClO^- \rightarrow NH_2Cl + OH^-$$

What is the balanced redox reaction?

_____

3. One type of Breathalyzer detects whether ethanol is in the breath of a person. Ethanol is oxidized to acetaldehyde by dichromate ions in acidic solution. The dichromate ion in solution is orange, while the Cr^{3+} aqueous ion is green. The appearance of a green color in the Breathalyzer test shows that the breath exceeds the legal limit of alcohol. The equation is

$$H^+ + Cr_2O_7^{2-} + C_2H_5OH \rightarrow Cr^{3+} + C_2H_4O + H_2O$$

Balance this redox reaction.

_____

4. Diluted hydrochloric acid can be used to remove limestone (calcium carbonate) surrounding phosphate and silicate fossils. The reaction produces carbon dioxide, water, and aqueous calcium chloride. Write the balanced chemical equation. Is it a redox reaction? Explain.

_____

_____

Name _____ Date _____ Class _____

miniLAB 21
Corrosion

Comparing and Contrasting A lot of money is spent every year correcting and preventing the effects of corrosion. Corrosion is a real-world concern of which everyone needs to be aware.

Materials iron nails (4); magnesium ribbon (2 pieces, each about 5 cm long); copper metal (2 pieces, each about 5 cm long); 150-mL beakers (4); distilled water; saltwater solution; sandpaper

Procedures

1. Use the sandpaper to buff the surfaces of each nail. Wrap two nails with the magnesium ribbon and two nails with the copper. Wrap the metals tightly enough so that the nails do not slip out.

2. Place each of the nails in a separate beaker. Add distilled water to one of the beakers containing a copper-wrapped nail and one of the beakers containing a magnesium-wrapped nail. Add enough distilled water to just cover the wrapped nails. Add salt water to the other two beakers. Record your observations for each of the beakers.

3. Let the beakers stand overnight in the warmest place available. Examine the nails and solutions the next day and record your observations.

Analysis

1. Describe the difference between copper-wrapped nails in the distilled water and salt water after standing overnight.

_____

_____

2. Describe the difference between the magnesium-wrapped nails in the distilled water and salt water.

_____

_____

3. In general, what is the difference between a copper-wrapped nail and a magnesium-wrapped nail?

_____

_____

CHEMLAB 21

Voltaic Cell Potentials

A voltaic cell converts chemical energy into electrical energy. It consists of two parts called half-cells. When two different metals, one in each half-cell, are used in the voltaic cell, a potential difference is produced. In this experiment, you will measure the potential difference of various combinations of metals used in voltaic cells and compare these values to the values found in the standard reduction potentials table.

Problem

How can you measure the potential of voltaic cells?

Objectives

- **Construct** voltaic cells using various combinations of metals for electrodes.
- **Design** the arrangement of the voltaic cells in a microplate in such a way as to use materials efficiently.
- **Determine** which metals are the anode and cathode in voltaic cells.
- **Compare** the experimental cell potential to the theoretical value found in **Table 21-1**.

Materials

metal strips (approximately 0.6 cm by 1.3 cm) of copper, aluminum, zinc, and magnesium
1M copper(II) nitrate
1M aluminum nitrate
1M zinc nitrate
1M magnesium nitrate
24-well microplate
Beral-type pipettes (5)

CBL System
voltage probe
filter paper (6 pieces size 0.6 cm by 2.5 cm)
1M potassium nitrate
forceps
steel wool or sandpaper
table of standard reduction potentials

Safety Precautions

- **Always wear goggles and a lab apron.**
- **The chemicals used in this experiment are eye and skin irritants. Wash thoroughly if they are spilled on the skin.**

Pre-Lab

1. Read the entire **CHEMLAB.**

2. Plan and organize how you will arrange voltaic cells in the 24-well microplate using the four metal combinations so that your time and materials will be used in the most efficient manner possible. Have your instructor approve your plan before you begin the experiment.

3. Prepare all written materials that you will take into the laboratory. Be sure to include safety precautions and procedure notes. Use the data table on the next page.

4. Review the definition of a voltaic cell.

_____

_____

5. Review the purpose of a salt bridge in the voltaic cell. In this experiment, the filter paper strips soaked in potassium nitrate are the salt bridges.

_____

_____

_____

CHEMLAB 21

6. Review the equation to calculate cell potential.

_____

7. For the voltaic cell Mg | Mg^{2+} ‖ Hg^{2+} | Hg, identify which metal is the anode and which metal is the cathode. Which metal is being oxidized and which metal is being reduced? What is the theoretical potential for this voltaic cell?

_____

_____

8. Review the equation to calculate percent error.

_____

_____

_____

Procedure

1. Prepare the CBL to read potential differences (voltage). Plug the voltage probe into Channel 1. Turn the CBL on. Push the MODE button once to activate the voltmeter function.

2. Soak the strips of filter paper in 2 mL of potassium nitrate solution. These are the salt bridges

for the experiment. Use forceps to handle the salt bridges.

3. Using the plan from your Pre-Lab, construct voltaic cells using the four metals and 1 mL of each of the solutions. Remember to minimize the use of solutions. Put the metals in the wells that contain the appropriate solution (for example, put the zinc metal in the solution with zinc nitrate). Use a different salt bridge for each voltaic cell. If you get a negative value for potential difference, switch the leads of the probe on the metals.

4. Record which metals are the anode and cathode in each cell in the data table. The black lead of the probe will be attached to the metal that acts as the anode. The red lead will be attached to the cathode.

5. Record the cell potential of each cell.

Cleanup and Disposal

1. Use forceps to remove the metals from the microplate.

2. Rinse the solution off the metal pieces with water, then use steel wool or sandpaper to clean them.

3. Rinse the wells of the microplate.

4. Return each metal to its correct container.

	Anode metal (black)	Cathode metal (red)	Actual cell potential (V)	Anode half-reaction and theoretical potential	Cathode half-reaction and theoretical potential	Theoretical cell potential	% Error
Voltaic Cell Potential Data							
1							
2							
3							
4							
5							
6							

CHEMLAB ㉑

Analyze and Conclude

1. **Applying Concepts** Write the half-reactions for the anode and cathode in each of the voltaic cells in the data table. Look up the half-reaction potentials from the standard reduction potentials table (**Table 21-1**) and record these in the data table.

2. **Using Numbers** Calculate the theoretical potential for each voltaic cell and record it in the data table.

3. **Predicting** Using your data table, rank the metals you used in order of most active to least active.

_____

_____

4. **Using Models** Calculate the percent error of the voltaic cell potential.

5. **Error Analysis** Why is the percent error calculated in step 4 large for some voltaic cells and small for others?

_____

_____

Real-World Chemistry

1. Why is lithium metal becoming a popular electrode in modern batteries? Use the standard reduction potentials table to help you answer this question.

_____

_____

_____

2. What type of battery is used in pacemakers to regulate a patient's heartbeat? What are some of the benefits of this battery?

_____

_____

miniLAB 22
Synthesis and Reactivity of Ethyne

Observing and Inferring Ethyne, often called *acetylene*, is used as a fuel in welding torches. In this lab, you will generate ethyne from the reaction of calcium carbide with water.

Materials 150-mL beaker, stirring rod, liquid dishwashing detergent, calcium carbide, forceps, wood splints, matches, ruler about 40 cm long, rubber band, phenolphthalein solution

Procedure 🥽 🧤 🚫 🧼 ☠️

1. Use a rubber band to attach a wood splint to one end of the ruler so that about 10 cm of the splint extends beyond the stick.

2. Place 120 mL water in the beaker and add 5 mL dishwashing detergent. Mix thoroughly.

3. Use forceps to pick up a pea-sized lump of calcium carbide (CaC_2). Do not touch the CaC_2 with your fingers. **CAUTION:** *If CaC_2 dust touches your skin, wash it away immediately with a lot of water.* Place the lump of CaC_2 in the beaker of detergent solution.

4. Use a match to light the splint while holding the ruler at the opposite end. Immediately bring the burning splint to the bubbles that have formed from the reaction in the beaker. Extinguish the splint after observing the reaction.

5. Use the stirring rod to dislodge a few large bubbles of ethyne and determine whether they float upward or sink in air.

6. Rinse the beaker thoroughly, then add 25 mL distilled water and a drop of phenolphthalein solution. Use forceps to place a small piece of CaC_2 in the solution. Observe the results.

Analysis

1. Describe your observations in steps 3 and 4. Could ethyne be used as a fuel?

_____

_____

2. Based on your observations in step 5, what can you infer about the density of ethyne compared to the density of air?

_____

3. The reaction of calcium carbide with water yields two products. One is ethyne gas (C_2H_2). From your observation in step 6, suggest what the other product is, and write a balanced chemical equation for the reaction.

_____

_____

_____

CHEMLAB 22

Analyzing Hydrocarbon Burner Gases

The fuel that makes a Bunsen burner work is a mixture of alkane hydrocarbons. One type of fuel is natural gas, whose primary component is methane (CH_4). The other type is called LP gas and consists primarily of propane (C_3H_8). In this experiment, you will use the ideal gas equation to help identify the main component of your classroom fuel supply.

Problem

What type of alkane gas is used in the burner fuel supplied to your laboratory?

Objectives

• **Measure** a volume of gas by water displacement.
• **Measure** the temperature, pressure, and mass at which the volume of the gas was measured.
• **Calculate** the molar mass of the burner gas using the ideal gas equation.

Materials

barometer
thermometer
1-L or 2-L plastic
 soft drink bottle
 with cap
burner tubing

pneumatic trough
100-mL graduated
 cylinder
balance (0.01g)
paper towels

Safety Precautions

• Always wear safety goggles and a lab apron.
• Be certain that there are no open flames in the lab.

Pre-Lab

1. Read the entire **CHEMLAB**.

2. Prepare all written materials that you will take into the laboratory. Include safety precautions and procedure notes. Use the data table on the next page.

3. Use the formulas of methane, ethane, and propane to calculate the compounds' molar masses.

_____

_____

4. Given *R* and gas pressure, volume, and temperature, show how you will rearrange the ideal gas equation to solve for moles of gas.

_____

_____

5. Suppose that your burner gas contains a small amount of ethane (C_2H_6). How will the presence of this compound affect your calculated molar mass if the burner gas is predominantly:

a. methane

_____

_____

b. propane

_____

_____

6. Use the data table on the next page.

Copyright © Glencoe/McGraw-Hill, a division of the McGraw-Hill Companies, Inc.

CHEMLAB (22)

Procedure

1. Connect the burner tubing from the gas supply to the inlet of the pneumatic trough. Fill the trough with tap water. Open the gas valve slightly and let a little gas bubble through the tank in order to flush all of the air out of the tubing.

2. Measure the mass of the dry plastic bottle and cap. Record the mass in the data table (bottle + air). Record both the barometric pressure and the air temperature.

3. Fill the bottle to overflowing with tap water and screw on the cap. If some air bubbles remain, tap the bottle gently on the desktop until all air has risen to the top. Take off the cap, add more water, and recap the bottle.

4. Place the thermometer in the trough. Invert the capped bottle into the pneumatic trough and remove the cap while keeping the mouth of the bottle underwater. Hold the mouth of the bottle directly over the inlet opening of the trough.

5. Slowly open the gas valve and bubble gas into the inverted bottle until all of the water has been displaced. Close the gas valve immediately. Record the temperature of the water.

6. While the bottle is still inverted, screw on the cap. Remove the bottle from the water. Thoroughly dry the outside of the bottle.

7. Measure the mass of the bottle containing the burner gas and record the mass in the data table (bottle + burner gas).

8. Place the bottle in a fume hood and remove the cap. Compress the bottle several times to expel most of the gas. Refill the bottle to overflowing with water and determine the volume of the bottle by pouring the water into a graduated cylinder. Record the volume of the bottle.

Cleanup and Disposal

1. Be certain that all gas valves are closed firmly and dump water out of pneumatic troughs.

2. Clean up water spills and dispose of materials as directed by your teacher.

3. Return all lab equipment to its proper place.

Mass and Volume Data	
Mass of bottle + air (g)	
Mass of air (g)	
Mass of "empty" bottle (g)	
Mass of bottle + collected burner gas (g)	
Mass of collected burner gas (g)	
Barometric pressure (atm)	
Temperature (°C)	
Temperature (K)	
Volume of gas collected (L)	

Analyze and Conclude

1. Acquiring Information Use the volume of the bottle and look up the density of air to compute the mass of the air the bottle contains. Use gas laws to compute the density of air at the temperature and pressure of your laboratory. The density of air at 1 atm and 20°C is 1.205 g/L.

2. Using Numbers Calculate the mass of the empty bottle by subtracting the mass of air from the mass of the bottle and air combined.

3. Using Numbers Determine the mass of the collected gas by subtracting the mass of the empty bottle from the mass of the bottle and gas.

CHEMLAB (22)

4. Interpreting Data Use the volume of gas, water temperature, and barometric pressure along with the ideal gas law to calculate the number of moles of gas collected.

_____

_____

_____

_____

_____

_____

5. Using Numbers Use the mass of gas and the number of moles to calculate the molar mass of the gas.

_____

_____

6. Drawing a Conclusion How does your experimental molar mass compare with the molar masses of methane, ethane, and propane? Suggest which of these gases are in the burner gas in your laboratory.

_____

7. Error Analysis If your experimental molar mass does not agree with that of any one of the three possible gases, suggest possible sources of error in the experiment. What factor other than error could produce such a result?

_____

_____

_____

Real-World Chemistry

1. Substances called *odorants* are mixed with natural gas before it is distributed to homes, businesses, and institutions. Why must an odorant be used, and what substances are used as odorants?

_____

_____

_____

2. At 1 atm and 20°C, the densities of methane and propane are 0.65 g/L and 1.83 g/L, respectively. Would either gas tend to settle in a low area such as the basement of a home? Explain.

_____

miniLAB 23

Making an Ester

Observing and Inferring Flowers and fruits have pleasant odors partly because they contain substances called esters. Companies make blends of synthetic esters to mimic the flavors and fragrances of esters found in nature. In this experiment, you will make an ester that has a familiar smell.

Materials salicylic acid, methanol, distilled water, 10-mL graduated cylinder, Beral pipette, 250-mL beaker, concentrated sulfuric acid, top or bottom of a petri dish, cotton ball, small test tube, balance, weighing paper, hot plate, test-tube holder

Procedure

1. Prepare a hot-water bath by pouring 150 mL of tap water into a 250-mL beaker. Place the beaker on a hot plate set at medium.

2. Place 1.5 g of salicylic acid in a small test tube and add 3 mL of distilled water. Then add 3 mL of methanol and 3 drops of concentrated sulfuric acid to the test tube. **CAUTION:** *Sulfuric acid is corrosive. Handle with care.*

3. When the water is hot but not boiling, place the test tube in the bath for 5 minutes.

4. Place the cotton ball in the petri dish half. Pour the contents of the test tube onto the cotton ball. Record your observation of the odor of the product.

_____

Analysis

1. The ester you produced has the common name oil of wintergreen. Write a chemical equation using names and structural formulas for the reaction that produced the ester.

_____

_____

_____

2. What are the advantages and disadvantages of using synthetic esters in consumer products as compared to using natural esters?

_____

_____

_____

_____

3. Name some products that you think could contain the ester you made in this experiment.

_____

CHEMLAB **23**

Properties of Alcohols

Alcohols are organic compounds that contain the −OH functional group. In this experiment, you will determine the strength of intermolecular forces of alcohols by determining how fast various alcohols evaporate. The evaporation of a liquid is an endothermic process, absorbing energy from the surroundings. This means that the temperature will decrease as evaporation occurs.

Problem

How do intermolecular forces differ in three alcohols?

Objectives

• **Measure** the rate of evaporation for water and several alcohols.
• **Infer** the relative strength of intermolecular forces of alcohols from rate of evaporation data.

Materials

thermometer
stopwatch
facial tissue
cloth towel
Beral pipettes (5)
methanol
ethanol (95%)

2-propanol (99%)
wire twist tie or
 small rubber band
piece of cardboard
 for use as a fan

Safety Precautions

• **Always wear safety goggles and a lab apron.**
• **The alcohols are flammable. Keep them away from open flames.**

Pre-Lab

1. Read the entire **CHEMLAB.**

2. Prepare all written materials that you will take into the laboratory. Be sure to include safety precautions and procedure notes. Use the data table on the next page.

3. Draw structural formulas for the three alcohols you will use in this activity. Describe how the structures of these compounds are alike and how they are different.

_____

_____

_____

_____

4. What types of forces exist between these kinds of molecules? Suggest which alcohol may have the greatest intermolecular forces.

_____

Procedure

1. Cut out five 2-cm by 6-cm strips of tissue.

2. Place a thermometer on a folded towel lying on a flat table so that the bulb of the thermometer extends over the edge of the table. Make sure the thermometer cannot roll off the table.

3. Wrap a strip of tissue around the bulb of the thermometer. Secure the tissue with a wire twist tie placed above the bulb of the thermometer.

4. Choose one person to control the stopwatch and read the temperature on the thermometer. A second person will put a small amount of the liquid to be tested into a Beral pipette.

5. When both people are ready, squeeze enough liquid onto the tissue to completely saturate it. At the same time, the other person starts the stopwatch, reads the temperature, and records it in the data table.

6. Fan the tissue-covered thermometer bulb with a piece of cardboard or other stiff paper. After one minute, read and record the final temperature in the data table. Remove the tissue and wipe the bulb dry.

Copyright © Glencoe/McGraw-Hill, a division of the McGraw-Hill Companies, Inc.

7. Repeat steps 3 through 6 for each of the three alcohols: methanol, ethanol, and 2-propanol. If your teacher has another alcohol, use it also.

Cleanup and Disposal

1. Place tissues in the trash. Pipettes can be reused.

Analyze and Conclude

1. Communicating Formulate a statement that summarizes your data, relating temperature change to the substances tested. Do not draw any conclusions yet.

Evaporation Data			
Substance	**Starting temp (°C)**	**Temp after 1 minute (°C)**	**ΔT (°C)**
Water			
Methanol			
Ethanol			
2-Propanol			
Other alcohol			

_____

_____

2. Acquiring and Analyzing Information Explain why the temperatures changed during the experiment.

_____

_____

3. Observing and Inferring What can you conclude about the relationship between heat transfer and the differences in the temperature changes you observed?

_____

_____

4. Drawing Conclusions Assume that the three alcohols have approximately the same molar enthalpy of vaporization. What can you say about the relative rates of evaporation of the three alcohols?

_____

_____

5. Drawing Conclusions Consider your answer to question 4. What can you conclude about the relative strength of intermolecular forces existing in the three alcohols?

_____

_____

6. Predicting Suppose you also tested the alcohol 1-pentanol in this experiment. Where among the alcohols tested would you predict 1-pentanol to rank in rate of evaporation from fastest to slowest? Describe the temperature change you would expect to observe. Explain your reasoning.

_____

_____

7. Thinking Critically Molar enthalpies of vaporization for the three alcohols are given in the table on the right. Note that they are not the same. In what way, if any, does this data change your conclusion about intermolecular forces?

_____

_____

_____

_____

Molar Enthalpies of Vaporization	
Substance	Enthalpy of vaporization at 25°C (kJ/mol)
Methanol	37.4
Ethanol	42.3
2-Propanol	45.4

8. Observing and Inferring Make a general statement comparing the molecular size of an alcohol in terms of the number of carbons in the carbon chain to the rate of evaporation of that alcohol.

_____

_____

9. Error Analysis Suggest a way to make this experiment more quantitative and controlled.

_____

_____

Real-World Chemistry

1. How can this experiment help explain why small-chain alcohols have a warning label indicating that they are flammable?

_____

_____

2. Would you expect to see such a warning label on a bottle of 1-decanol? Explain.

_____

3. A mixture of 70% 2-propanol (isopropanol) and 30% water is sold as rubbing alcohol, which may be used to help reduce a fever. Explain how this process works.

_____

_____

_____

4. Why do you suppose that 2-propanol is a component in some products used to soothe sunburned skin?

_____

miniLAB 24
A Saponification Reaction

Applying Concepts The reaction between a triglyceride and a strong base such as sodium hydroxide is called saponification. In this reaction, the ester bonds in the triglyceride are hydrolyzed by the base. The sodium salts of the fatty acids, called soaps, precipitate out, and glycerol is left in solution.

Materials solid vegetable shortening, 250-mL beaker, 600-mL beaker, 6.0M NaOH, ethanol, saturated NaCl solution, stirring rod, hot plate, tongs, 25-mL graduated cylinder, evaporating dish, cheesecloth (20 cm × 20 cm), funnel

Procedure

1. Place a 250-mL beaker on the hot plate. Add 25 g solid vegetable shortening to the beaker. Turn the hot plate on at a medium setting.

2. As the vegetable shortening melts, slowly add 12 mL ethanol and then 5 mL 6.0M NaOH to the beaker. **CAUTION:** *Ethanol is flammable. NaOH causes skin burns. Wear gloves.*

3. Heat the mixture, stirring occasionally, for about 15 minutes, but do not allow it to boil.

4. When the mixture begins to thicken, use tongs to remove the beaker from the heat. Allow the beaker to cool for 5 minutes, then place it in a cold-water bath in the 600-mL beaker.

5. Add 25 mL saturated NaCl solution to the mixture in the beaker. The soap is not very soluble and will appear as small clumps.

6. Collect the solid soap clumps by filtering them through a cheesecloth-lined funnel.

7. Using gloved hands, press the soap into an evaporating dish. Allow the soap to air dry for 1 or 2 days.

8. Remove your gloves and wash your hands.

Analysis

1. What type of bonds present in the triglycerides are broken during the saponification reaction?

_____

2. What is the common name for the sodium salt of a fatty acid?

_____

3. How does soap remove dirt from a surface?

_____

_____

_____

_____

4. Write a word equation for the saponification reaction in this lab.

CHEMLAB 24

Alcoholic Fermentation in Yeast

Yeast cells are able to metabolize many types of sugars. In this experiment, you will observe the fermentation of sugar by baker's yeast. When yeast cells are mixed with a sucrose solution, they must first hydrolyze the sucrose to glucose and fructose. Then the glucose is broken down in the absence of oxygen to form ethanol and carbon dioxide. You can test for the production of carbon dioxide by using a CBL pressure sensor to measure an increase in pressure.

Problem

What is the rate of alcoholic fermentation of sugar by baker's yeast?

Objectives

- **Measure** the pressure of carbon dioxide produced by the alcoholic fermentation of sugar by yeast.
- **Calculate** the rate of production of carbon dioxide by the alcoholic fermentation of sugar by yeast.

Materials

CBL system
graphing calculator
ChemBio program
Vernier pressure
  sensor
link cable
CBL-DIN cable
test tube with #5
  rubber-stopper
  assembly
5% sucrose solution

ring stand
stirring rod
600-mL beaker
thermometer
basting bulb
hot and cold water
yeast suspension
vegetable oil
utility clamp
10-mL graduated
  cylinders (2)
pipette

Safety Precautions

- Always wear safety goggles and a lab apron.
- Do not use the thermometer as a stirring rod.

Pre-Lab

1. Reread the section of this chapter that describes alcoholic fermentation.

2. Write the chemical equation for the alcoholic fermentation of glucose.

_____

_____

3. Read the entire **CHEMLAB.**

4. Prepare all written materials that you will take into the laboratory. Be sure to include safety precautions and procedure notes.

5. Form a hypothesis about how the pressure inside the test tube is related to the production of carbon dioxide during the reaction. Refer to the ideal gas law in your explanation.

_____

_____

_____

_____

CHEMLAB ㉔

6. Why is temperature control an essential feature of the **CHEMLAB**?

_____

_____

_____

_____

_____

_____

Procedure

1. Load the ChemBio program into your graphing calculator. Connect the CBL and calculator with the link cable. Connect the pressure sensor to the CBL with a CBL-DIN cable.

2. Prepare a water bath using the 600-mL beaker. The beaker should be about two-thirds full of water. The water temperature should be between 36°C and 38°C.

3. Set up the test tube, ring stand, and utility clamp. Obtain about 3 mL yeast suspension in a 10-mL graduated cylinder, and pour it into the test tube. Obtain about 3 mL 5% sucrose solution in a 10-mL graduated cylinder. Add the sucrose solution to the yeast in the test tube. Stir to mix. Pour enough vegetable oil on top of the mixture to completely cover the surface.

4. Place the stopper assembly into the test tube. Make sure it has an airtight fit. Leave both valves of the assembly open to the atmosphere.

5. While one lab partner does step 5, the other partner should do steps 6 and 7. Lower the test tube into the water bath and allow it to incubate for 10 minutes. Keep the temperature of the water bath between 36°C and 38°C by adding small amounts of hot or cold water with the basting bulb as needed.

6. Start the ChemBio program. Choose 1:SET UP PROBES under MAIN MENU. Choose 1 for number of probes. Choose 3:PRESSURE under SELECT PROBE. Enter 1 for Channel. Choose 1:USE STORED for CALIBRATION. Choose 1:ATM for PRESSURE UNITS.

7. Choose 2:COLLECT DATA under MAIN MENU. Choose 2:TIME GRAPH under DATA COLLECTION. Use time between sample seconds = 10. Use number of samples = 60. (This will give you 600 seconds or 10 minutes of data). Choose 1:USE TIME SETUP under CONTINUE? Set Ymin = 0.8, Ymax = 1.3, and Yscl = 0.1. Do not press ENTER until the test tube has finished incubating.

8. After the test tube has incubated for 10 minutes, close the valve attached to the stopper. Make sure the valve near the pressure sensor is open to the sensor. Start measuring the gas pressure by pressing ENTER. Monitor the pressure reading on the CBL unit. If the pressure exceeds 1.3 atm, the stopper can pop off. Open the air valve on the pressure sensor to release this excess gas pressure.

9. After 10 minutes, the data collection will stop. Open the air valve on the stopper. If needed, you can run a second trial by closing the air valve and choosing 2:YES to REPEAT? If you are finished, press 1:NO.

Cleanup and Disposal

1. Rinse out and wash all items.

2. Rinse the yeast suspension/sucrose/vegetable oil mixture down the sink with large amounts of water.

3. Return all lab equipment to its proper place.

CHEMLAB 24

Analyze and Conclude

1. **Making and Using Graphs** Choose 3:VIEW GRAPH from the MAIN MENU. Make a sketch of the graph. (You also may want to record the data table by using 4:VIEW DATA.)

2. **Interpreting Data** The rate of carbon dioxide production by the yeast can be found by calculating the slope of the graph. Return to the MAIN MENU and choose 5:FIT CURVE. Choose 1:LINEAR L1, L2. The slope will be listed under LINEAR as "A" of $Y = A*X + B$. Record this value.

_____

3. **Communicating** How does your rate of carbon dioxide production compare with the rates of other members of the class?

_____

4. **Analyzing** Why did you add vegetable oil to the test tube in step 3?

_____

_____

5. **Error Analysis** Suppose that the pressure does not change during a trial. What might be some possible reasons for this?

_____

_____

_____

_____

Real-World Chemistry

1. Yeast is used in baking bread because the carbon dioxide bubbles make the bread rise. The other product of alcoholic fermentation is ethanol. Why can't you taste this alcohol when you eat bread?

_____

2. How would the appearance of a loaf of bread be different if you used twice as much yeast as the recipe called for?

_____

_____

miniLAB 25

Modeling Radioactive Decay

Formulating Models Because of safety concerns, it is usually not possible to directly experiment with radioactive isotopes in the class-room. Thus, in this lab, you will use pennies to model the half-life of a typical radioactive isotope. Each penny represents an individual atom of the radioisotope.

Materials 100 pennies, 5-oz or larger plastic cup, graph paper, graphing calculator (optional)

Procedure

1. Place the pennies in the plastic cup.

2. Place your hand over the top of the cup and shake the cup several times.

3. Pour the pennies onto a table. Remove all the pennies that are "heads-up." These pen-nies represent atoms of the radioisotope that have undergone radioactive decay.

4. Count the number of pennies that remain ("tails-up" pennies) and record this number in the Decay Results data table as the Number of pennies remaining for trial 1.

5. Place all of the "tails-up" pennies back in the plastic cup.

6. Repeat steps 2 through 5 for as many times as needed until no pennies remain.

Decay Results	
Trial number	Number of pennies remaining
0	100
1	
2	
3	
4	
5	
6	
7	
8	

Analysis

1. Make a graph of Trial number versus Number of pennies remaining from the Decay Results data table. Draw a smooth curve through the plotted points.

_____

_____

_____

2. How many trials did it take for 50% of the sample to decay? 75%? 90%?

_____

_____

_____

3. If the time between each trial is 1 minute, what is the half-life of the radioisotope?

_____

_____

4. Suppose that instead of using pennies to model the radioisotope, you use 100 dice. After each toss, any die that comes up a "6" represents a decayed atom and is removed. How would the result using the dice compare with the result obtained from using the pennies?

_____

_____

CHEMLAB 25

Measuring Naturally Occurring Radiation

As you may know, some common everyday substances are radioactive. In this lab, you will investigate the three naturally occurring potassium isotopes found in a common store-bought salt substitute. Two of potassium's isotopes, potassium-39 (93.1%) and potassium-41 (6.89%) are stable. However, potassium-40 (0.01%) decays by beta emission to form stable calcium-40. You will first measure the background radiation level, and then use that information to determine the radiation due to the beta decay of potassium-40. You will also measure radiation at various locations around your school.

Problem

How can you determine if a substance contains radioactive isotopes?

Objectives

- **Measure** background radiation and radiation emitted by a radioactive isotope.
- **Compare** the level of background radiation to the level of radiation emitted by a radioactive isotope.

Materials

CBL system
RADIATIN software
  program
graphing calculator
link-to-link cable
Student Radiation
  Monitor

CBL-P adapter
TI GRAPH LINK
petri dish (with lid)
salt substitute or
  pure potassium
  chloride (KCl)
balance

Safety Precautions

- **Always wear safety goggles and a lab apron.**

Pre-Lab

1. Read the entire **CHEMLAB.**

2. Prepare all written materials that you will take into the laboratory. Include any necessary safety precautions and procedure notes. Use the data table on the next page.

3. What is an isotope? A radioactive isotope?

_____

_____

_____

_____

_____

_____

_____

4. Write the nuclear equation for the radioactive decay of potassium-40 by beta emission. Identify the "parent" and "daughter" nuclides in the decay.

_____

_____

_____

Copyright © Glencoe/McGraw-Hill, a division of the McGraw-Hill Companies, Inc.

CHEMLAB 25

5. Using nuclide-stability rules, form a hypothesis that explains why calcium-40 should be a more stable nuclide than potassium-40.

_____

_____

_____

_____

_____

Procedure

1. Load the program RADIATIN into the graphing calculator.

2. Connect the graphing calculator to the CBL system using the link-to-link cable. Connect the CBL system to the Student Radiation Monitor using the CBL-P adapter. Turn on all devices. Set the Student Radiation Monitor on the audio setting and place it on top of an empty petri dish.

3. Start the RADIATIN program. Go to MAIN MENU. Select 4:SET NO. SAMPLE. Choose 20 for the number of samples in each reading. Press ENTER.

4. Select 1:COLLECT DATA from the MAIN MENU. Select 4:TRIGGER/PROMPT from the COLLECTING MODE menu. Press ENTER to begin collecting data. After a few seconds, the calculator will ask you to enter a PROMPT. Enter 1 (because this is the first data point) and press ENTER. Choose 1:MORE DATA under TRIGGER/PROMPT.

5. Press ENTER to begin the next data point. A graph will appear. When asked to enter the next PROMPT, enter the number that appears at the top right corner of the calculator screen, and then press ENTER. Choose 1:MORE DATA under TRIGGER/PROMPT.

6. Repeat step 5 until you have at least five data points. This set of data is the background level of radiation from natural sources.

7. Use the balance to measure out 10.0 g salt substitute or pure potassium chloride (KCl). Pour the substance into the center of the petri dish so that it forms a small mound. Place the Student Radiation Monitor on top of the petri dish so that the Geiger Tube is positioned over the mound. Repeat step 5 until you have at least five data points.

8. When you are finished collecting data, choose 2:STOP AND GRAPH under TRIGGER/PROMPT. The data points (PROMPTED) are stored in L1, the counts per minute (CTS/MIN) are stored in L2. Press ENTER to view a graph of data.

Cleanup and Disposal

1. Return the salt substitute or potassium chloride (KCl) used in the experiment to the container prepared by your instructor.

2. Disconnect the lab setup and return all equipment to its proper place.

Radiation Level Data	
Data point	**Counts/min**

CHEMLAB **25**

Analyze and Conclude

1. **Collecting Data** Record the data found in L1 and L2 (STAT, EDIT) in the Radiation Level Data table.

2. **Graphing Data** Graph the data from L1 and L2. Use the graph from the graphing calculator as a guide.

3. **Interpreting Data** What is the average background radiation level in counts/minute?

_____

4. **Interpreting Data** What is the average radiation level in counts/minute for the potassium-40 isotope found in the salt substitute?

_____

5. **Observing and Inferring** How can you explain the difference between the background radiation level and the radiation level of the salt substitute?

_____

_____

6. **Thinking Critically** Is the data for the background radiation and the radiation from the potassium-containing sample consistent or random in nature? Propose an explanation for the pattern or lack of pattern seen in the data.

_____

_____

_____

_____

_____

_____

_____

_____

7. **Error Analysis** Describe several ways to improve the experimental procedure so it yields more accurate radiation level data.

_____

_____

_____

_____

_____

Copyright © Glencoe/McGraw-Hill, a division of the McGraw-Hill Companies, Inc.

CHEMLAB (25)

Real-World Chemistry

1. Arrange with your teacher to plan and perform a field investigation using the experimental setup from this experiment to measure the background level radiation at various points around school or around town. Propose an explanation for your findings.

_____

_____

_____

2. Using the procedure in this lab, determine if other consumer products contain radioisotopes. Report on your findings.

_____

_____

_____

_____

_____

_____

_____

miniLAB 26
Acid Rain in a Bag

Making a Model Acid precipitation often falls to Earth hundreds of kilometers away from where the pollutant gases enter the atmosphere because the gases diffuse through the air and are carried by the wind. In this lab, you will model the formation of acid rain to observe how the damage caused by acid varies with the distance from the source of pollution. You also will observe another factor that affects the amount of damage caused by acid rain.

Materials plastic petri dish bottom; 1-gallon zipper-close, plastic bag; white paper; droppers; 0.04% bromocresol green indicator; 0.5M KNO$_2$; 1.0M H$_2$SO$_4$; clock or watch

Procedure

1. Place 25 drops of 0.04% bromocresol green indicator of varying sizes in the bottom half of a plastic petri dish so that they are about 1 cm apart. Be sure that there are both large and small drops at any given distance from the center. Leave the center of the petri dish empty.

2. Place a zipper-close, plastic bag on a piece of white paper.

3. Carefully slide the petri dish containing the drops of indicator inside the plastic bag.

4. In the center of the petri dish, place 1 large drop of 0.5M KNO$_2$. To this KNO$_2$ drop, add 2 drops of 1.0M H$_2$SO$_4$. **CAUTION:** *KNO$_2$ and H$_2$SO$_4$ are skin irritants.* Carefully seal the bag. Observe whether the mixing of these two chemicals produces any bubbles of gas. This is the pollution source.

5. Observe and compare the color changes that take place in the drops of indicator of different sizes and distances from the pollution source. Record your observations every 15 seconds.

6. To clean up, carefully remove the petri dish from the bag, rinse it with water, then dry it.

Analysis

1. As the gas reacts with water in the drops, two acids form, 2NO$_2$ + H$_2$O → HNO$_3$ + HNO$_2$. What are these acids?

_____

2. Did the small or large drops change color first? Why?

_____

3. Did the distance of the indicator drops from the pollution source have an effect on how quickly the reaction occurred? Explain.

_____

_____

4. State two hypotheses that will explain your observations, and incorporate the answers from questions 2 and 3 in your hypotheses.

_____

_____

miniLAB

Acid Rain in a Bag, *continued*

5. Based on your hypotheses in question 4, what can you infer about the damage done to plants by acid fog as compared with acid rain?

_____

_____

CHEMLAB 26

Solar Pond

If you made a list of popular types of alternative energy sources, solar energy probably would be near the top. Of course, the energy we use from all sources ultimately originates from the Sun. It would seem that solar energy would be the easiest to use. The problem is how to store solar energy when the Sun is not shining. In this experiment, you will investigate one method that could be used to trap and store solar energy.

Problem

Build a small-scale model of a solar pond and test how it traps and stores solar energy.

Objectives

- **Construct** a small-scale solar pond using simple materials.
- **Collect** temperature data as the solar pond model heats and cools.
- **Hypothesize** as to why a solar pond is able to trap and store energy.

Materials

CBL System
graphing calculator
ChemBio program
link-to-link cable
temperature probes (2)
150-watt lightbulb
socket and clamp for bulb
black plastic frozen-dinner dish

waterproof tape
table salt
hot plate
stirring rod
250-mL beaker
beaker tongs
TI GRAPH LINK (optional)
ring stand and clamp
250-mL graduated cylinder

Safety Precautions

- **The lightbulb will become hot when it is turned on.**
- **Do not touch the hot plate while it is on.**

Pre-Lab

1. Read the entire **CHEMLAB.**

2. Prepare all written materials that you will take into the laboratory. Include safety precautions and procedure notes.

3. Water is transparent to visible light but opaque to infrared radiation. How do you think these properties will affect your solar pond model?

_____

_____

_____

4. If you used only tap water in your model, convection currents would bring warmer, less dense water from the bottom to the surface. Do you think this will happen with your solar pond model? Explain your answer.

_____

_____

_____

5. Predict which of the two layers of the model will have the higher final temperature. Explain your prediction.

_____

_____

_____

_____

_____

Procedure

1. Prepare a saturated table salt (NaCl) solution by heating 100 mL of tap water in a beaker on a hot plate. When the water is boiling, slowly add enough table salt to saturate the solution while stirring with a stirring rod. Remove the beaker from the hot plate with beaker tongs and allow the solution to cool slowly overnight.

2. The next day, prepare the solar pond model. Place the black plastic dish on the lab bench where you want to run the experiment. Use a small piece of waterproof tape to attach one of the temperature probes to the bottom of the black plastic dish. Plug this probe into Channel 1 of the CBL System. Slowly pour the 100 mL of saturated salt solution into the dish.

3. Carefully add about 100 mL of tap water on top of the saturated salt-water layer in the dish. Use care not to mix the two layers. Suspend the end

of the second temperature probe in the tap-water layer and plug it into Channel 2 of the CBL System.

4. Connect the graphing calculator to the CBL System using the link cable. Turn on both units. Run the ChemBio program. Choose 1:SET UP PROBES under MAIN MENU. Choose 2 probes. Under SELECT PROBE, choose 1:TEMPERA-TURE. Enter 1 for Channel. This is for the probe at the bottom of the salt-water layer. Under SELECT PROBE, choose 1: TEMPERATURE. Enter 2 for Channel. This is for the probe in the tap-water layer.

5. Under MAIN MENU, choose 2: COLLECT DATA. Choose 2: TIME GRAPH. For time between samples in seconds, choose 30. For number of samples, choose 60. This will allow the experiment to run for 30 minutes. Set the calculator to use this time setup. Input the following: $Ymin = 0$, $Ymax = 30$, $Yscl = 1$. Do not start collecting data yet.

6. Position the 150-watt lightbulb about 15 to 20 cm over the top of the solar pond model. Turn on the light. Press ENTER on the calculator to begin collecting data. After about 6 to 8 minutes, turn off the lightbulb and move it away from the solar pond model. Do not disturb the experiment until the calculator is finished with its 30-minute run.

Cleanup and Disposal

Rinse the salt solution off the temperature probes.

Analyze and Conclude

1. **Graphing Data** Make a copy of the graph from the graphing calculator. If you have TI GRAPH LINK and a computer, do a screen print.

2. Interpreting Graphs Describe the shape of each curve in the graph of time versus temperature before and after the lightbulb was turned off. Explain the significance of the difference.

_____

_____

_____

3. Comparing and Contrasting Which layer of your solar pond model did the best job of trapping and storing heat?

_____

4. Applying Concepts Why does the graph of time versus temperature decrease more rapidly near the surface when the lightbulb is turned off?

_____

_____

5. Forming a Hypothesis Make a hypothesis to explain what is happening in your model.

_____

_____

6. Designing an Experiment How would you test your hypothesis?

_____

_____

7. Error Analysis How might your results have been different if you had used a white dish by mistake instead of a black dish? Explain.

_____

_____

Real-World Chemistry

1. Water in a lake rises to the surface when heated and sinks to the bottom when cooled in a process called convection. Compare and contrast the density of the water as it rises with the density of the water as it sinks.

_____

2. The El Paso Solar Pond was the first in the world to successfully use solar pond technology to store and supply heat for industrial processes. It was built with three main layers: a top layer that contains little salt, a middle layer with a salt content that increases with depth, and a very salty bottom layer that stores the heat. Which layer has the greatest density? The least density? Why doesn't the storage layer in the El Paso Solar Pond cool by convection?

_____

_____

CHEMLAB AND MINILAB WORKSHEETS
Answer Key

CHEMLAB 1

The Rubber Band Stretch

Galileo Galilei (1564–1642) was an Italian philosopher, astronomer, and mathematician. Galileo pioneered the use of a systematic method of observation, experimentation, and analysis as a way to discover facts about nature. Modern science has its roots in Galileo's 17th-century work on the art of experimentation. This chapter introduced you to how scientists approach their work. In this CHEMLAB, you will have a chance to design a scientific method to study something you have observed many times before—the stretching of a rubber band.

Problem

What happens when you heat a stretched rubber band?

Objectives

- **Observe** the properties of a stretched and a relaxed rubber band.
- **Form a hypothesis** about the effect of heat on a stretched rubber band.
- **Design** an experiment to test your hypothesis.
- **Collect** and **analyze** data.
- **Draw conclusions** based on your analysis.

Materials

large rubber band
500-g mass
ring stand
clamp
hair dryer
meterstick or ruler

Safety Precautions

- Frequently observe the rubber band for any splits. Discard if rubber band is defective.
- The hair dryer can become hot, so handle it with care.

Pre-Lab

1. Heat is the transfer of energy from a warmer object to a cooler object. If an object feels warm to your finger, your finger is cooler than the object and energy is being transferred from the object to your finger. In what direction does the energy flow if an object feels cooler to you? **from the warmer object (your finger) to the cooler one (the object)**

2. Your forehead is very sensitive to hot and cold. How can you use this fact to detect whether an object is giving off or absorbing heat? **The sensitive skin on the forehead tells that an object is giving off heat if it feels warm on your forehead and absorbing heat if it feels cool.**

3. Read the entire CHEMLAB. It is important to know exactly what you are going to do during all chemistry experiments so you can use your laboratory time efficiently and safely. What is the problem that this experiment is going to explore? **What happens when you heat a stretched rubber band?**

4. What typical steps in a scientific method will you use to explore the problem? Write down the procedure that you will use in each experiment that you design. Be sure to include all safety precautions. **Check student procedures to assure they follow a correct scientific method.**

---

miniLAB 1

Developing Observation Skills

Observing and Inferring A chemist's ability to make careful and accurate observations is developed early. The observations often are used to make inferences. An inference is an explanation or interpretation of observations.

Materials petri dish (2), graduated cylinder, whole milk, water, vegetable oil, four different food colorings, toothpick (2), dishwashing detergent

Procedure

1. Add water to a petri dish to a height of 0.5 cm. Add 1 mL of vegetable oil.
2. Dip the end of a toothpick in liquid dishwashing detergent.
3. Touch the tip of the toothpick to the water at the center of the petri dish. Record your detailed observations.
4. Add whole milk to a second petri dish to a height of 0.5 cm.
5. Place one drop each of four different food colorings in four different locations on the surface of the milk. Do not put a drop of food coloring in the center.
6. Repeat steps 2 and 3.

Analysis

1. What did you observe in step 3? **The oil moved away from the detergent.**

2. What did you observe in step 6? **The colors moved to the outside of the dish.**

3. Oil, the fat in milk, and grease belong to a class of chemicals called lipids. What can you infer about the addition of detergent to dishwater? **It helps remove grease and oil from items being washed.**

Expected Results: When the toothpick touches the milk, the detergent temporarily destroys the surface tension. The colors move to the outside of the dish. The detergent emulsifies any fat in the milk. Convectionlike currents are established, causing the colors to move from the outside toward the center.

CHEMLAB 1

5. You will need to record the data that you collect during each experiment. Use the data tables below.

Rubber Band Data

Experiment #	Observations
Trial 1	
Trial 2	
Trial 3	
Trial 4	

Rubber Band Data

Experiment #	Observations
Trial 1	
Trial 2	
Trial 3	
Trial 4	

Rubber Band Data

Experiment #	Observations
Trial 1	
Trial 2	
Trial 3	
Trial 4	

Procedure

1. Obtain one large rubber band. Examine the rubber band for any splits or cracks. If you find any defects, discard it and obtain a new one.
2. Record detailed observations of the unstretched rubber band.
3. Design your first experiment to observe whether heat is given off or absorbed by a rubber band as it is stretched. Have your teacher approve your plan.
4. Do repeated trials of your experiment until you are sure of the results. **CAUTION:** *Do not bring the rubber band near your face unless you are wearing goggles.*
5. Design a second experiment to observe whether heat is given off or absorbed by a rubber band as it contracts after being stretched. Have your teacher approve your plan.
6. Do repeated trials of your experiment until you are sure of the results.
7. Use your observations in steps 2, 4, and 6 to form a hypothesis and make a prediction about what will happen to a stretched rubber band when it is heated.
8. Use the remaining items in the list of materials to design a third experiment to test what happens to a stretched rubber band as it is heated. Have your teacher approve your plan. Be sure to record all observations before, during, and after heating.

Cleanup and Disposal

1. Return the rubber band to your teacher to be reused by other classes.
2. Allow the hair dryer to cool before putting it away.

Expected Results: Observations should reflect that a rubber band gives off heat when it stretches, absorbs heat when it contracts, and contracts when heated.

Analyze and Conclude

1. **Observing and Inferring** What results did you observe in step 4 of the procedure? Was energy gained or lost by the rubber band? By your forehead? Explain. **The rubber band feels warm. Energy was lost by the rubber band and gained by the forehead.**

CHEMLAB 1

2. **Observing and Inferring** What results did you observe in step 6 of the procedure? Was energy gained or lost by the rubber band? By your forehead? Explain. **The rubber band feels cooler. Heat is gained by the rubber band and lost by the forehead.**

3. **Applying** Many substances expand when they are heated. Did the rubber band behave in the same way? How do you know? **When heated, a stretched rubber band contracts.**

4. **Drawing a Conclusion** Did the result of heating the stretched rubber band in step 8 confirm or refute your hypothesis? Explain. **Most students would hypothesize that the rubber band would stretch when heated. The actual result refuted the hypothesis. The rubber band became shorter.**

5. **Making Predictions** What would happen if you applied ice to the stretched rubber band? Predictions should include that it would stretch.

6. **Error Analysis** Compare your results and conclusion with those of your classmates. What were your independent and dependent variables? Did you use a control? Did all of the lab teams measure the same variables? Were the data that you collected qualitative or quantitative? Does this make a difference when reporting your data to others? Do your results agree? Why or why not? **Student controls and variables will vary by student and by experiment. Sample answers might be: independent variable—degree of stretching; dependent variable—temperature; control—temperature of an unstretched rubber band. The data are qualitative because no actual measurements were made. A source of error might be time lags after stretching the rubber bands that allow temperature to change.**

Real-World Chemistry

1. When you put ice in a glass so that the ice rises higher than the rim, water does not overflow the glass when the ice melts. Explain. **Water expands when frozen. When ice melts, the water takes up less volume.**

2. Why do you think temperature extremes must be taken into account when bridges and highways are designed? **The materials that make up the bridge expand in warm weather and contract in cold weather. Bridge materials will crack if nothing is done to allow the bridge to expand and contract.**

CHEMLAB 2

Using Density to Find the Thickness of a Wire

The thickness of wire often is measured using a system called the American Wire Gauge (AWG) standard. The smaller the gauge number, the larger the diameter of the wire. For example, 18-gauge copper wire has a diameter of about 0.102 cm; 12-gauge copper wire has a diameter of about 0.205 cm. Such small diameters are difficult to measure accurately with a metric ruler. In this experiment, you will plot measurements of mass and volume to find the density of copper. Then, you will use the density of copper to confirm the gauge of copper wire.

Problem

How can density be used to verify the diameter of copper wire?

Objectives

- **Collect** and **graph** mass and volume data to find the density of copper.
- **Measure** the length and volume of a copper wire, and **calculate** its diameter.
- **Calculate** percent errors for the results.

Materials

tap water
100-mL graduated cylinder
small cup, plastic
balance
copper shot
copper wire (12-gauge, 18-gauge)
metric ruler
pencil
graph paper
graphing calculator (optional)

Safety Precautions

- Always wear safety goggles and a lab apron.

Pre-Lab

1. Read the entire CHEMLAB.
2. What is the equation used to calculate density?
   density = mass/volume
3. How can you find the volume of a solid that has an irregular shape?
   by water displacement
4. What is a meniscus and how does it affect volume readings?
   It is the curved surface of a liquid. The bottom of the meniscus is considered to be the level of the liquid.
5. If you plot mass versus volume, what property of matter will the slope of the graph represent?
   density
6. How do you find the slope of a graph? **Choose two points on the line. Divide the difference in the y values by the difference in the x values.**
7. A piece of copper wire is a narrow cylinder. The equation for the volume of a cylinder is
   $$V = \pi r^2 h$$
   where V is the volume, r is the radius, h is the height, and π (pi) is a constant with a value of 3.14. Rearrange the equation to solve for r.
   $$r = \sqrt{V/(\pi h)}$$

---

miniLAB 2

Density of an Irregular Solid

Measuring To calculate density, you need to know both the mass and volume of an object. You can find the volume of an irregular solid by displacing water.

Materials balance, graduated cylinder, water, washer or other small object

Procedure

1. Find and record the mass of the washer.
2. Add about 15 mL of water to your graduated cylinder. Measure and record the volume. Because the surface of the water in the cylinder is curved, make volume readings at eye level and at the lowest point on the curve. The curved surface is called a *meniscus*.
3. Carefully add the washer to the cylinder. Then measure and record the new volume.

Analysis

1. Use the initial and final volume readings to calculate the volume of the washer.
   $V_{final} - V_{initial} = V_{washer}$
2. Use the calculated volume and the measured mass to find the density of the washer.
   mass/volume = density
3. Explain why you cannot use displacement of water to find the volume of a sugar cube.
   Sugar dissolves in water.
4. The washer is a short cylinder with a hole in the middle. Describe another way to find its volume.
   Measure the diameter of the washer and calculate its area. Measure the diameter of the hole and calculate its area. Subtract the area of the hole from the area of the washer. Multiply the answer by the thickness of the washer.

Expected Result: Density is determined in g/mL by dividing mass by volume.

CHEMLAB 2

8. What is the relationship between the diameter and the radius of a cylinder?

$d = 2r$

9. Use the two data tables below.

Sample Data

Density of Copper

Trial	Mass of copper added	Total mass of copper	Total volume of water displaced
1	9.7 g	9.7 g	1.0 mL
2	9.9 g	19.6 g	2.0 mL
3	12.4 g	32.0 g	3.4 mL
4	12.2 g	44.2 g	4.8 mL

Diameter of Copper Wire

	12-gauge	18-gauge
Length	16.3 cm	16.4 cm
Mass	4.8 g	1.2 g
Measured diameter	0.20 cm	0.10 cm
Calculated diameter	0.21 cm	0.10 cm

Procedure

Record all measurements in the data tables.

1. Pour about 20 mL of water into a 100-mL graduated cylinder. Read the actual volume.
2. Find the mass of the plastic cup.
3. Add about 10 g of copper shot to the cup and find the mass again.
4. Pour the copper shot into the graduated cylinder and read the new volume.
5. Repeat steps 3 and 4 three times. By the end of the four trials, you will have about 40 g of copper in the graduated cylinder.
6. Obtain a piece of 12-gauge copper wire and a piece of 18-gauge copper wire. Use a metric ruler to measure the length and diameter of each wire.
7. Wrap each wire around a pencil to form a coil. Remove the coils from the pencil. Find the mass of each coil.

Cleanup and Disposal

1. Carefully drain off most of the water from the graduated cylinder. Make sure all of the copper shot remains in the cylinder.
2. Pour the copper shot onto a paper towel to dry. Both the copper shot and wire can be reused.

Analyze and Conclude

1. Using Numbers Complete the table for the density of copper by calculating the total mass of copper and the total water displaced for each trial.
See Density of Copper table.

2. Making and Using Graphs Graph total mass versus total volume of copper. Draw a line that best fits the points. Then use two points on your line to find the slope of your graph. Because density equals mass divided by volume, the slope will give you the density of copper.
Density should equal approximately 8.96 g/cm³.

If you are using a graphing calculator, select the 5:FIT CURVE option from the MAIN MENU of the ChemBio program. Choose 1:LINEAR L1.L2 from the REGRESSION/LIST to help you plot and calculate the slope of the graph.

CHEMLAB 2

3. Using Numbers Calculate the percent error for your value of density.

$\% \text{ error} = (D_{actual} - D_{calculated})/D_{actual} \times 100\%$

4. Using Numbers To complete the second data table, you must calculate the diameter for each wire. Use the accepted value for the density of copper and the mass of each wire to calculate volume. Then use the equation for the volume of a cylinder to solve for the radius. Double the radius to find the diameter.
See Diameter of Copper Wire table.

5. Comparing and Contrasting How do your calculated values for the diameter compare to your measured values and to the AWG values listed in the introduction?
Answers should be close to the values listed.

6. Error Analysis How could you change the procedure to reduce the percent error for density?
Answers might include using a smaller graduated cylinder so volume readings will be more accurate.

Real-World Chemistry

1. There is a standard called the British Imperial Standard Wire Gauge (SWG) that is used in England and Canada. Research the SWG standard to find out how it differs from the AWG standard. Are they the only standards used for wire gauge?
Gauge 9 SWG is 0.144 in. and gauge 9 in AWG is 0.1144 in. AWG is also called Brown and Sharp. Other gauges include Birmingham or Stubbs, Washburn and Moen, metric wire gauge, and U.S. Government Standard.

2. Interview an electrician or a building inspector who reviews the wiring in new or re-modeled buildings. Ask what the codes are for the wires used and how the diameter of a wire affects its ability to safely conduct electricity. Ask to see a wiring diagram.
Check students' results for consistency. Local electrical codes may vary. The National Electrical Code provides criteria for all electrical installations. Color codes for wires help electricians make correct connections. Wire is characterized by gauge number (diameter) and kind of insulation. Improper wire size may cause fire.

CHEMLAB 3

Matter and Chemical Reactions

One of the most interesting characteristics of matter, and one that drives the study and exploration of chemistry, is the fact that matter changes. By examining a dramatic chemical reaction, such as the reaction of the element copper and the compound silver nitrate in a water solution, you can readily observe chemical change. Drawing on one of the fundamental laboratory techniques introduced in this chapter, you can separate the products. Then, you will use a flame test to confirm the identity of the products.

Problem

Is there evidence of a chemical reaction between copper and silver nitrate? If so, which elements reacted and what is the name of the compound they formed?

Objectives

- **Observe** the reactants as they change into product.
- **Separate** a mixture by filtration.
- **Predict** the names of the products.

Materials

copper wire
$AgNO_3$ solution
sandpaper
stirring rod
50-mL graduated cylinder
50-mL beaker
funnel
filter paper

250-mL Erlenmeyer flask
ring stand
small iron ring
plastic petri dish
paper clip
Bunsen burner
tongs

Safety Precautions

- Always wear safety goggles, gloves, and a lab apron.
- Silver nitrate is toxic and will harm skin and clothing.
- Use caution around a flame.

Pre-Lab

1. Read the entire CHEMLAB.
2. Prepare all written materials that you will take into the laboratory. Be sure to include safety precautions and procedure notes. Use the data table on the next page.
3. Define the terms physical property and chemical property. Give an example of each.
   A physical property is a characteristic that can be observed or measured without changing the substance's composition—for example, color, shape, or mass. A chemical property is the ability of a substance to combine with or change into one or more other substances—for example, reactivity with water.
4. Form a hypothesis regarding what you might observe if
   a. a chemical change occurs.
      You might observe a change in color or odor, the evolution of heat or light, the absorption of energy, or the formation of a gas, liquid, or different solid. A different product will form.
   b. a physical change occurs.
      You might observe a change in shape or in physical state, such as boiling, condensing, freezing, melting, evaporating, dissolving, or crystallizing.

---

miniLAB 3

Separating Ink Dyes

Applying Concepts Chromatography is an important diagnostic tool for chemists. Many types of substances can be separated and analyzed using this technique. In this experiment, you will use paper chromatography to separate the dyes in water-soluble black ink.

Materials 9-oz wide-mouth plastic cups (2); round filter paper; 1/4 piece of 11-cm round filter paper; scissors; pointed object, approximately 3–4 mm diameter; water-soluble black felt pen or marker

Procedure

1. Fill one of the wide-mouth plastic cups with water to about 2 cm from the top. Wipe off any water drops on the lip of the cup.
2. Place the round filter paper on a clean, dry surface. Make a concentrated ink spot in the center of the paper by firmly pressing the tip of the pen or marker onto the paper.
3. Use a sharp object to create a small hole, approximately 3–4 mm or about the diameter of a pen tip, in the center of the ink spot.
4. Roll the 1/4 piece of filter paper into a tight cone. This will act as a wick to draw the ink. Work the pointed end of the wick into the hole in the center of the round filter paper.
5. Place the paper/wick apparatus on top of the cup of water, with the wick in the water. The water will move up the wick and outward through the round paper.
6. When the water has moved to within about 1 cm of the edge of the paper (about 20 minutes), carefully remove the paper from the water-filled cup and put it on the empty cup.

Expected Results: As the water spreads out on the paper, different dyes in the ink will spread out from the center and be deposited on the filter paper at different distances from the center.

Analysis

1. Make a drawing of the round filter paper and label the color bands. How many distinct dyes can you identify?
   Drawings should resemble the miniLab photo with correct labels.

2. Why do you see different colors at different locations on the filter paper?
   Different components of the ink have varying attraction for the filter paper. Therefore, the colors that comprise the ink will be deposited at different distances from the center of the paper.

3. How does your chromatogram compare with those of your classmates who used other types of black felt pens or markers? Explain the differences.
   Answers will vary. Different makes and types of black ink have different dyes in them.

CHEMLAB 3

5. Distinguish between a homogeneous mixture and a heterogeneous mixture.

A homogeneous mixture is one in which one or more substances are evenly distributed throughout another substance. A heterogeneous mixture is one in which there is an observable separation of component substances.

Tear corner

Procedure

1. Obtain 8 cm of copper wire. Rub the copper wire with the sandpaper until it is shiny.

2. Measure approximately 25 mL $AgNO_3$ (silver nitrate) solution into a 50-mL beaker. **CAUTION:** *Do not allow to contact skin or clothing.*

3. Make and record an observation of the physical properties of the copper wire and $AgNO_3$ solution.

4. Coil the piece of copper wire to a length that will fit into the beaker. Make a hook on the end of the coil to allow the coil to be suspended from the stirring rod.

5. Hook the coil onto the middle of the stirring rod. Place the stirring rod across the top of the beaker immersing some of the coil in the $AgNO_3$ solution.

6. Make and record observations of the wire and the solution every five minutes for 20 minutes.

7. Use the ring stand, small iron ring, funnel, Erlenmeyer flask, and filter paper to set up a filtration apparatus. Attach the iron ring to the ring stand. Adjust the height of the ring so the end of the funnel is inside the neck of the Erlenmeyer flask.

8. To fold the filter paper, examine the diagram above. Begin by folding the circle in half, then fold in half again. Tear off the lower right corner of the flap that is facing you. This will help the filter paper stick better to the funnel. Open the folded paper into a cone. Place the filter paper cone in the funnel.

9. Remove the coil from the beaker and dispose of it as directed by your teacher. Some of the solid product may form a mixture with the liquid in the beaker. Decant the liquid by slowly pouring it down the stirring rod into the funnel. Solid product will be caught in the filter paper. Collect the filtrate—the liquid that runs through the filter paper—in the Erlenmeyer flask.

10. Transfer the clear filtrate to a petri dish.

11. Adjust a Bunsen burner flame until it is blue. Hold the paper clip with tongs in the flame until no additional color is observed. **CAUTION:** *The paper clip will be very hot.*

12. Using tongs, dip the hot paper clip in the filtrate. Then, hold the paper clip in the flame. Record the color you observe.

Reaction Observations	
Time (min)	Observations
5	Students should observe gradual formation of gray solid on the copper
10	wire. The solution will turn blue-green.
15	
20	
	Flame test: blue-green color

CHEMLAB 3

Cleanup and Disposal

1. Dispose of materials as directed by your teacher.

2. Clean and return all lab equipment to its proper place.

3. Wash hands thoroughly.

Analyze and Conclude

1. **Classifying** Which type of mixture is silver nitrate in water? Which type of mixture is formed in step 6? Explain.

   homogeneous; heterogeneous and homogeneous

2. **Observing and Inferring** Describe the changes you observed in step 6. Is there evidence a chemical change occurred? Why?

   A grayish solid formed on the wire. The solution turned blue-green. Yes, a solid formed and a color change occurred.

3. **Predicting** Predict the products formed in step 6. You may not know the exact chemical name, but you should be able to make an intuitive prediction.

   silver and copper nitrate

4. **Using Resources** Use resources such as the *CRC Handbook of Chemistry and Physics*, the *Merck Index*, or the Internet to determine the colors of silver metal and copper nitrate in water. Compare this information with your observations of the reactants and products in step 6.

   Silver metal is white to gray. Copper nitrate is blue-green.

5. **Identifying** Metals emit characteristic colors in flame tests. Copper emits a blue-green light. Do your observations in step 12 confirm the presence of copper in the filtrate collected in step 9?

   Experimental results should agree with blue-green light.

6. **Communicating** Express in words the chemical equation that represents the reaction that occurred in step 6.

   Copper and silver nitrate solution react to form silver and copper nitrate.

7. **Error Analysis** Compare your recorded observations with those of several other lab teams. Explain any differences.

   Copper wire may not have been clean. The better observations will be more detailed.

Real-World Chemistry

1. Analytical chemists determine the chemical composition of matter. Two major branches of analytical chemistry are qualitative analysis—determining what is in a substance—and quantitative analysis—measuring how much substance. Research and report on a career as an analytical chemist in the food industry.

   Answers will vary but may include analysis of vitamin content, flavors, preservatives, or calorie content.

Name _____ Date _____ Class _____

miniLAB 4
Modeling Isotopes

Formulating Models Because they have different compositions, pre- and post-1982 pennies can be used to model an element with two naturally occurring isotopes. From the penny "isotope" data, the mass of each penny isotope and the average mass of a penny can be determined.

Materials bag of pre- and post-1982 pennies, balance

Procedure

1. Get a bag of pennies from your teacher, and sort the pennies by date into two groups: pre-1982 pennies and post-1982 pennies. Count and record the total number of pennies and the number of pennies in each group.

2. Use the balance to determine the mass of ten pennies from each group. Record each mass to the nearest 0.01 g. Divide the total mass of each group by ten to get the average mass of a pre- and post-1982 penny "isotope."

Analysis

1. Using data from step 1, calculate the percentage abundance of each group. To do this, divide the number of pennies in each group by the total number of pennies. **The relative number of pre- and post-1982 pennies in the bag determines the percentage abundance of each group. The two abundances must sum to 100%.**

2. Using the percentage abundance of each "isotope" and data from step 2, calculate the atomic mass of a penny. To do this, use the following equation for each "isotope."

   mass contribution = (% abundance)(mass)

   Sum the mass contributions to determine the atomic mass. **The atomic mass of a penny depends upon the mixture of pennies each student receives. Sample data is shown here.**

   mass contribution (pre-1982) = (55.0%)(3.11 g) = 1.71 g
   mass contribution (post-1982) = (45.0%)(2.55 g) = 1.15 g
   atomic mass = (1.71 g + 1.15 g) = 2.86 g

3. Would the atomic mass be different if you received another bag of pennies containing a different mixture of pre- and post-1982 pennies? Explain. **Atomic mass is dependent upon the relative abundance of each isotope. A different mixture of pennies would have a different atomic mass.**

4. In step 2, instead of measuring and using the mass of a single penny of each group, the average mass of each type of penny was determined. Explain why. **Masses of individual pennies will vary due to wear. Using an average mass of each penny minimizes the errors related to the variation.**

Expected Results:
Pre-1982 pennies have a greater mass than post-1982 pennies.

Mass of ten pre-1982 pennies = 31.10 g

Average mass of a pre-1982 penny = 3.11g

Mass of ten post-1982 pennies = 25.48 g

Average mass of a post-1982 penny = 2.55 g

The atomic mass depends on the mixture analyzed.

Name _____ Date _____ Class _____

CHEMLAB 4
Very Small Particles

This laboratory investigation will help you conceptualize the size of an atom. You will experiment with a latex balloon containing a vanilla bean extract. Latex is a polymer, meaning that it is a large molecule (a group of atoms that act as a unit) that is made up of a repeating pattern of smaller molecules. The scent of the vanilla extract will allow you to trace the movement of its molecules through the walls of the solid latex balloon.

Problem
How small are the atoms that make up the molecules of the balloon and the vanilla extract? How can you conclude the vanilla molecules are in motion?

Objectives
- **Observe** the movement of vanilla molecules based on detecting their scent.
- **Infer** what the presence of the vanilla scent means in terms of the size and movement of its molecules.
- **Formulate models** that explain how small molecules in motion can pass through an apparent solid.
- **Hypothesize** about the size of atoms that make up matter.

Materials
vanilla extract or flavoring
9-inch latex balloon (2)
dropper

Safety Precautions

- Always wear safety goggles and a lab apron.
- Be careful not to cut yourself when using a sharp object to deflate the balloon.

Pre-Lab

1. Read the entire CHEMLAB.
2. Describe a polymer and give an example. **A polymer is a large molecule made up of many repeating smaller molecules. Latex is an example.**
3. Identify constants in the experiment. **The amount of vanilla placed into each balloon is constant. The chemical composition of the balloons is constant.**

CHEMLAB 4

4. What is the purpose of the vanilla extract? **The purpose of the vanilla flavoring is to trace the movement of molecules using the sense of smell to detect their presence.**

5. As a liquid evaporates, predict what you think will happen to the temperature of the remaining liquid. **The high-energy molecules leave first, lowering the average kinetic energy of the remaining liquid. It is cooler.**

6. When you smell an aroma, is your nose detecting a particle in the solid, liquid, or gas phase? **You are smelling a gas or vapor.**

7. Prepare all written materials that you will take into the laboratory. Be sure to include safety precautions and procedure notes. Use the data table below to record your data and observations.

balloon is in danger of bursting. Try to keep the vanilla in one location as the balloon is inflated. Tie the balloon closed.

3. Feel the outside of the balloon where the vanilla is located and note the temperature of this area relative to the rest of the balloon. Record your observations in the data table.

4. Use only air to inflate a second balloon to approximately the same size as that of the first, and tie it closed. Feel the outside of the second balloon. Make a relative temperature comparison to that of the first balloon. Record your initial observations.

5. Place the inflated balloons in a small, enclosed area such as a closet or student locker.

6. The next day, repeat the observations in steps 3 and 4 after the vanilla has dried inside the balloon. Record these final observations.

7. To avoid splattering your clothes with dark brown vanilla, do not deflate the balloon until the vanilla has dried inside.

Cleanup and Disposal

1. After the vanilla has dried, deflate the balloon by puncturing it with a sharp object.

2. Dispose of the pieces of the balloon as directed by your teacher.

Data Table			
Observations		Initial	Final
Balloon 1 with vanilla	Relative size	Same size	Same size
	Relative temperature	Cool	Room temp.
Balloon 2 without vanilla	Relative size	Same size	Same size
	Relative temperature	Room temp.	Room temp.

Analyze and Conclude

1. **Observing and Inferring** How did the relative volumes of balloons 1 and 2 change after 24 hours? **The volume of the balloons did not change.**

CHEMLAB 4

2. **Observing and Inferring** By comparing the relative temperatures of balloons 1 and 2, what can you conclude about the temperature change as the vanilla evaporated? Explain. **Balloon 1 feels cool to the touch. The vanilla absorbs energy from the surroundings in changing to a vapor.**

3. **Observing and Inferring** Did the vanilla's odor get outside the balloon and fill the enclosed space? Explain. **The vanilla's odor is outside the balloon and fills the small, enclosed space. The vanilla vaporizes and its molecules move through the pores in the wall of the balloon.**

4. **Predicting** Do you think vanilla will leak more rapidly from a fully inflated balloon or from a half-inflated balloon? Explain. **Vanilla will leak more rapidly from a fully inflated balloon. The thinner wall will allow more vanilla to pass through its pores because the polymer chains are stretched farther apart.**

5. **Hypothesizing** Write a hypothesis that explains your observations. **See the Solutions Manual or Teacher Wraparound Edition.**

6. **Comparing and Contrasting** Compare your hypothesis to Dalton's atomic theory. In what ways is it similar? How is it different? **Dalton's atomic theory states that all matter is composed of extremely small particles. So does the hypothesis in question 5. The laboratory investigation does not address the many other aspects of Dalton's atomic theory.**

7. Error Analysis What factors might affect the results of different groups that performed the experiment? What types of errors might have occurred during the procedure? **Student answers will vary. Temperature and inflation of the balloon (tightness) will affect results. The balloon may not have been tightly closed.**

Real-World Chemistry

1. Explain why helium-filled, Mylar-foil balloons can float freely for several weeks, but latex balloons for less than 24 hours. **Metallic coated Mylar is a nonporous polymer film. Thus, helium does not escape from Mylar.**

2. How are high-pressure gases stored for laboratory and industrial use to prevent loss? **High-pressure gases are stored in impermeable steel storage cylinders.**

CHEMLAB 5

Line Spectra

You know that sunlight is made up of a continuous spectrum of colors that combine to form white light. You also have learned that atoms of gases can emit visible light of characteristic wavelengths when excited by electricity. The color you see is the sum of all of the emitted wavelengths. In this experiment, you will use a diffraction grating to separate these wavelengths into emission line spectra. You also will investigate another type of line spectrum—the absorption spectrum. The color of each solution you observe is due to the reflection or transmission of unabsorbed wavelengths of light. When white light passes through a sample and then a diffraction grating, dark lines show up on the continuous spectrum of white light. These lines correspond to the wavelengths of the photons absorbed by the solution.

Problem

What absorption and emission spectra do various substances produce?

Objectives

- **Observe** emission spectra of several gases.
- **Observe** the absorption spectra of various solutions.
- **Analyze** patterns of absorption and emission spectra.

Materials

(For each group)
ring stand with clamp
40-W tubular light-bulb
light socket with power cord
275-mL polystyrene culture flask (4)
Flinn C-Spectra® or similar diffraction grating

food coloring (red, green, blue, and yellow)
set of colored pencils
book

(For entire class)
spectrum tubes (hydrogen, neon, and mercury)
spectrum tube power supplies (3)

Safety Precautions

- Always wear safety goggles and a lab apron.
- Use care around the spectrum tube power supplies.
- Spectrum tubes will get hot when used.

Pre-Lab

1. Read the entire CHEMLAB.
2. Explain how electrons in an element's atoms produce an emission spectrum.

When electrons drop from higher-energy orbitals to lower-energy orbitals, the atom emits energy in the form of light. Each orbital transition is associated with a characteristic spectral line.

---

miniLAB 5

Flame Tests

Classifying When certain compounds are heated in a flame, they emit a distinctive color. The color of the emitted light can be used to identify the compound.

Materials Bunsen burner; cotton swabs (6); distilled water; crystals of lithium chloride, sodium chloride, potassium chloride, calcium chloride, strontium chloride, unknown

Procedure

1. Dip a cotton swab into the distilled water. Dip the moistened swab into the lithium chloride so that a few of the crystals stick to the cotton. Put the crystals on the swab into the flame of a Bunsen burner. Observe the color of the flame and record it in the data table.

2. Repeat step 1 for each of the metallic chlorides (sodium chloride, potassium chloride, calcium chloride, and strontium chloride). Be sure to record the color of each flame in your data table.

3. Obtain a sample of unknown crystals from your teacher. Repeat the procedure in step 1 using the unknown crystals. Record the color of the flame produced by the unknown crystals. Dispose of used cotton swabs as directed by your teacher.

Flame Test Results

Compound	Flame color
Lithium chloride	red
Sodium chloride	yellow
Potassium chloride	violet
Calcium chloride	red-orange
Strontium chloride	bright red
Unknown	depends on compound

Analysis

1. Each of the known compounds tested contains chlorine, yet each compound produced a flame of a different color. Explain why this occurred.
The colors are due primarily to electron transitions of the metal atoms. The colors are characteristic of lithium, sodium, potassium, calcium, and strontium.

2. How is the atomic emission spectrum of an element related to these flame tests?
The colors are a composite of each element's visible spectrum.

3. What is the identity of the unknown crystals? Explain how you know.
Answers will vary depending on the identity of the unknown sample.

CHEMLAB 5

3. Distinguish among a continuous spectrum, an emission spectrum, and an absorption spectrum. **A continuous spectrum contains a continuum of visible colors from red to violet. An absorption spectrum is a continuous spectrum containing black lines at wavelengths associated with the atoms' energy absorptions. An emission spectrum consists of colored lines associated with the atoms' energy-level transitions.**

4. Use the data tables below and on the next page.

Procedure

1. Use a Flinn C-Spectra® to view an incandescent lightbulb. What do you observe? Draw the spectrum using colored pencils.

2. Use the Flinn C-Spectra® to view the emission spectra from tubes of gaseous hydrogen, neon, and mercury. Use colored pencils to make drawings in the data table of the spectra observed.

3. Fill a 275-mL culture flask with about 100-mL water. Add 2 or 3 drops of red food coloring to the water. Shake the solution.

4. Repeat step 3 for the green, blue, and yellow food coloring. CAUTION: *Be sure to thoroughly dry your hands before handling electrical equipment.*

5. Set up the 40-W lightbulb so that it is near eye level. Place the flask with red food coloring about 8 cm from the lightbulb. Use a book or some other object to act as a stage to put the flask on. You should be able to see light from the bulb above the solution and light from the bulb projecting through the solution.

6. With the room lights darkened, view the light using the Flinn C-Spectra®. The top spectrum viewed will be a continuous spectrum of the white lightbulb. The bottom spectrum will be the absorption spectrum of the red solution. The black areas of the absorption spectrum represent the colors absorbed by the red food coloring in the solution. Use colored pencils to make a drawing in the data table of the absorption spectra you observed.

7. Repeat steps 5 and 6 using the green, blue, and yellow colored solutions.

Cleanup and Disposal

1. Turn off the light socket and spectrum tube power supplies.

2. Wait several minutes to allow the incandescent lightbulb and the spectrum tubes to cool.

3. Follow your teacher's instructions on how to dispose of the liquids and how to store the lightbulb and spectrum tubes.

Expected Results: For each colored solution listed below, all colors are visible except as noted.

Red solution: blue and green
Green solution: red and orange
Blue solution: yellow, orange, and some red
Yellow solution: blue

Drawings of Emission Spectra

Hydrogen	
Neon	
Mercury	

Blue Green Yellow Orange Red

CHEMLAB 5

Drawings of Absorption Spectra

Red	
Green	
Blue	
Yellow	

Analyze and Conclude

1. **Thinking Critically** How can the existence of spectra help to prove that energy levels in atoms exist? **The spectral lines indicate energy is absorbed or released as the atom transitions from one energy level to another.**

2. **Thinking Critically** How can the single electron in a hydrogen atom produce all of the lines found in its emission spectrum? **At any given time, the electron occupies a single orbital. However, it can move into other, vacant orbitals as the atom absorbs or emits energy.**

3. **Predicting** How can you predict the absorption spectrum of a solution by looking at its color? **The color of a solution is due to the color of light it transmits. The colors not transmitted are absorbed, and these colors comprise the absorption spectrum.**

4. **Thinking Critically** How can spectra be used to identify the presence of specific elements in a substance? **The spectrum of each element is unique. Thus, the presence of a unique atomic spectrum indicates the presence of that element.**

Real-World Chemistry

1. How can absorption and emission spectra be used by the Hubble space telescope to study the structures of stars or other objects found in deep space? **The light emitted by stars can be analyzed for the presence of unique atomic spectra. Such spectra can identify the types of matter that comprise the star.**

2. The absorption spectrum of chlorophyll *a* indicates strong absorption of red and blue wavelengths. Explain why leaves appear green. **Leaves appear green because they reflect (do not absorb) green light. The reflected green light is what our eyes see.**

Copyright © Glencoe/McGraw-Hill, a division of the McGraw-Hill Companies, Inc.

miniLAB 6

Periodicity of Molar Heats of Fusion and Vaporization

Making and Using Graphs The heats required to melt or to vaporize a mole (a specific amount of matter) are known as the molar heat of fusion (H_f) and the molar heat of vaporization (H_v), respectively. These heats are unique properties of each element. You will investigate if the molar heats of fusion and vaporization for the period 2 and 3 elements behave in a periodic fashion.

Materials either a graphing calculator, a computer graphing program, or graph paper; Appendix **Table C-6** or access to comparable element data references

Procedure

Use **Table C-6** in Appendix C to look up and record the molar heat of fusion and the molar heat of vaporization for the period 3 elements listed in the table. Then, record the same data for the period 2 elements.

Analysis

1. Graph molar heats of fusion versus atomic number. Connect the points with straight lines and label the curve. Do the same for molar heats of vaporization.

See sample graph in the Solutions Manual. Graphs should reflect data shown in data table.

2. Do the graphs repeat in a periodic fashion? Describe the graphs to support your answer.

Yes, both molar heat of fusion and vaporization repeat in a periodic fashion, and, therefore, are periodic properties of elements.

Molar Heat Data			
Element	Atomic number	H_f (kJ/mol)	H_v (kJ/mol)
Li	3	3	148
Be	4	7.9	298
B	5	50.2	504
C	6	104.6	711
N	7	0.072	5.58
O	8	0.44	6.82
F	9	0.51	6.54
Ne	10	0.34	1.77
Na	11	2.06	97.4
Mg	12	8.5	127
Al	13	10.7	291
Si	14	50.2	359
P	15	0.659	362
S	16	1.73	9.62
Cl	17	6.41	20.4
Ar	18	1.18	6.52

CHEMLAB 6

Descriptive Chemistry of the Elements

What do elements look like? How do they behave? Can periodic trends in the properties of elements be observed? You cannot examine all of the elements on the periodic table because of limited availability, cost, and safety concerns. However, you can observe several of the representative elements, classify them, and compare their properties. The observation of the properties of elements is called descriptive chemistry.

Problem

What is the pattern of properties of representative elements?

Objectives

- **Observe** properties of various elements.
- **Classify** elements as metals, nonmetals, and metalloids.
- **Examine** general trends within the periodic table.

Materials

stopped test tubes containing small samples of elements
plastic dishes containing samples of elements
conductivity apparatus
1.0M HCl
test tubes (6)
test-tube rack
10-mL graduated cylinder
spatula
small hammer
glass marking pencil

Safety Precautions

- Wear safety goggles and a lab apron at all times.
- Do not handle elements with bare hands.
- 1.0M HCl is harmful to eyes and clothing.
- Never test chemicals by tasting.
- Follow any additional safety precautions provided by your teacher.

Pre-Lab

1. Read the entire CHEMLAB.
2. Use the data table on the next page to record the observations you make during the lab.
3. Examine the periodic table. What is the physical state of most metals? Nonmetals? Metalloids? **All naturally occurring metals are solids, except for mercury, which is a liquid at room temperature. All metalloids are solids. Nonmetals are primarily gases and solids, with bromine being the only liquid.**
4. Look up the definitions of the terms luster, malleability, and electrical conductivity. To what elements do they apply? **Luster: shininess; malleability: capable of being flattened into sheets or formed into shapes; electrical conductivity: capable of transmitting an electric current; They are properties commonly associated with metals.**

CHEMLAB 6

Procedure

1. Observe and record the appearance of the element sample in each test tube. Observations should include physical state, color, and other characteristics such as luster and texture. **CAUTION:** *Do not remove the stoppers from the test tubes.*

2. Remove a small sample of each of the elements contained in a dish and place it on a hard surface designated by your teacher. Gently tap each element sample with a small hammer. **CAUTION:** *Safety goggles must be worn.* If the element is malleable, it will flatten. If it is brittle, it will shatter. Record your observations.

3. Use the conductivity tester to determine which elements conduct electricity. An illuminated lightbulb is evidence of electrical conductivity. Record your results in your data table. Clean the electrodes with water and make sure they are dry before testing each element.

4. Label each test tube with the symbol for one of the elements in the plastic dishes. Using a graduated cylinder, add 5 mL of water to each test tube.

5. Use a spatula to put a small amount of each of the six elements (approximately 0.2 g or a 1-cm long ribbon) into the test tube labeled with its chemical symbol. Using a graduated cylinder, add 5 mL of 1.0M HCl to each test tube. Observe each test tube for at least one minute. The formation of bubbles is evidence of a reaction between the acid and the element. Record your observations.

Cleanup and Disposal

Dispose of all materials as instructed by your teacher.

Observation of Elements

Element	Appearance and physical state	Malleable or brittle?	Reactivity with HCl	Electrical conductivity	Classification
carbon	gray/black, dull solid	brittle	no	yes	metalloid
oxygen	colorless gas	—	—	—	nonmetal
magnesium	shiny, silver solid	malleable	yes	yes	metal
silicon	shiny, gray solid	brittle	no	yes	metalloid
sulfur	dull, yellow solid	brittle	no	yes	nonmetal
chlorine	yellow-green gas	not tested	not tested	not tested	nonmetal

Analyze and Conclude

1. **Interpreting Data** Metals are usually malleable and good conductors of electricity. They are generally lustrous and silver or white in color. Many react with acids. Write the word "metal" beneath the Classification heading in the data table for those element samples that display the general characteristics of metals.

2. **Interpreting Data** Nonmetals can be solids, liquids, or gases. They do not conduct electricity and do not react with acids. If a nonmetal is a solid, it is likely to be brittle and have color (other than white or silver). Write the word "nonmetal" beneath the Classification heading in the data table for those element samples that display the general characteristics of nonmetals.

CHEMLAB 6

3. **Interpreting Data** Metalloids combine some of the properties of both metals and nonmetals. Write the word "metalloid" beneath the Classification heading in the data table for those element samples that display the general characteristics of metalloids.

4. **Making a Model** Construct a periodic table and label the representative elements by group (1A through 7A). Using the information in your data table and the periodic table, record the identities of elements observed during the lab in your periodic table. **See periodic table below.**

5. **Interpreting Data** Describe any trends among the elements you observed in the lab. **Students may note that the metallic characteristic increases from right-to-left, and from top-to-bottom.**

Real-World Chemistry

1. Why did it take so long to discover the first noble gas element? **Many elements were discovered by using electricity to break down compounds into their component elements. Because noble gases form virtually no compounds, the electrical decomposition technique could not be used.**

2. Research one of the most recently discovered elements. New elements are created in particle accelerators and tend to be very unstable. Because of this, many of the properties of a new element cannot be determined. Using periodic group trends in melting and boiling point, predict whether the new element you selected is likely to be a solid, liquid, or gas. **Answers will vary. For example, 114 may be a solid with high melting point.**

	1A	2A	3A	4A	5A	6A	7A
2				6, C, metalloid	7, N, nonmetal	8, O, nonmetal	
3		12, Mg, metal	13, Al, metal	14, Si, metalloid	15, P, nonmetal	16, S, nonmetal	17, Cl, nonmetal
4	20, Ca, metal				33, As, uncertain	34, Se, uncertain	
5				50, Sn, metal			53, I uncertain
6				82, Pb, metal			

Copyright © Glencoe/McGraw-Hill, a division of the McGraw-Hill Companies, Inc.

miniLAB 7

Properties of Magnesium

Observing and Inferring In this activity, you will mix magnesium with hydrochloric acid and observe the result.

Materials test tube, test-tube rack, 10-mL graduated cylinder, hydrochloric acid, magnesium ribbon, sandpaper, cardboard, wood splint, safety matches

Procedure 🥽 🧤 🔬 🚫 🔥

Record all of your observations.

1. Place your test tube in a test-tube rack. For safety, the test tube should remain in the rack throughout the lab.

2. Use a 10-mL graduated cylinder to measure out about 6 mL of hydrochloric acid. Pour the acid slowly into the test tube. **CAUTION:** *If acid gets on your skin, flush with cold running water. Use the eyewash station if acid gets in your eye.*

3. Use sandpaper to clean the surface of a 3-cm length of magnesium ribbon.

4. Drop the ribbon into the acid and immediately cover the test tube with a cardboard lid.

5. As the reaction appears to slow down, light a wood splint in preparation for step 6.

6. As soon as the reaction stops, uncover the test tube and drop the burning splint into it.

7. Pour the contents of the test tube into a container specified by your teacher. Then rinse the test tube with water. Do not place your fingers inside the unwashed tube.

Expected Results:
The sandpaper removes the oxide coating from the gray Mg ribbon, exposing a shiny silver-colored surface. When the Mg ribbon is dropped into the HCl solution in the test tube, the magnesium reacts with HCl and hydrogen gas bubbles are produced. The burning splint causes the gas to ignite. A sound is produced by the reaction of H_2 and O_2.

Analysis

1. Compare the appearance of the magnesium ribbon before and after you used the sandpaper. What did the sandpaper remove? **The gray coating from the Mg ribbon was removed to expose a shiny silver-colored surface.**

2. What happened when you placed the ribbon in the acid? How did you decide when the reaction was over? **Magnesium ribbon reacted with HCl to produce a gas. The bubbling stopped.**

3. What did you observe when you placed the burning splint in the test tube? **The burning splint ignited the gas.**

4. What gas can ignite explosively when exposed to oxygen in the air? (Hint: The gas is lighter than air.) **hydrogen**

CHEMLAB 7

Hard Water

The contents of tap water vary among communities. In some areas, the water is hard. Hard water is water that contains large amounts of calcium or magnesium ions. Hardness can be measured in milligrams per liter (mg/L) of calcium or magnesium ions. Hard water makes it difficult to get hair, clothes, and dishes clean. In this lab, you will learn how hard water is softened and how softening water affects its ability to clean. You will also collect, test, and classify local sources of water.

Problem

How can hard water be softened? How do hard and soft water differ in their ability to clean?

Objectives

• **Compare** the effect of distilled water, hard water, and soft water on the production of suds.
• **Calculate** the hardness of a water sample.

Materials

3 large test tubes with stoppers
test-tube rack
grease pencil
25-mL graduated cylinder
distilled water
dropper

hard water
250-mL beaker
balance
filter paper
washing soda
dish detergent
metric ruler

Safety Precautions

🥽 🧤 🔬

• Always wear safety goggles and a lab apron.
• Washing soda is a skin and eye irritant.

Pre-Lab

1. Read the entire CHEMLAB.

2. Hypothesize about the effect hard and soft water will have on the ability of a detergent to produce suds. Then, predict the relative sudsiness of the three soap solutions. **Students may hypothesize that hard water and detergent produce less suds and that relative sudsiness: distilled water > soft water > hard water.**

3. Use the data table on the next page.

4. Are there any other safety precautions you need to consider? **Safety glasses and lab apron; washing soda can irritate the skin and eyes.**

5. Suppose you accidentally add more than one drop of detergent to one of the test tubes. Is there a way to adjust for this error or must you discard the sample and start over? **You could adjust by adding the same number of additional drops of detergent to the other tubes.**

CHEMLAB 7

the balance to zero. Then measure about 0.2 g of washing soda. Remove the filter paper and washing soda. Reset the balance to zero.

6. Use the filter paper to transfer the washing soda to the beaker containing the remainder of the hard water. Swirl the mixture to soften the water. Record any observations.

7. Slowly pour soft water into test tube S until you reach the marked height.

8. Add one drop of dish detergent to each test tube. Stopper the tubes tightly. Then shake each sample to produce suds. Use a metric ruler to measure the height of the suds.

9. Collect water samples from reservoirs, wells, or rain barrels. Use the sudsiness test to determine the hardness of your samples. If access to a source is restricted, ask a local official to collect the sample.

Cleanup and Disposal

1. Use some of the soapy solutions to remove the grease marks from the test tubes.

2. Rinse all of the liquids down the drain with lots of tap water.

Sample Data

Production of Suds	
Sample	Level of Suds (cm)
Distilled water	5.5 cm
Hard water	4.0 cm
Soft water	9.0 cm

6. The American Society of Agricultural Engineers, the U.S. Department of the Interior, and the Water Quality Association agree on the following classification of water hardness. GPG stands for grains per gallon. One GPG equals 17.1 mg/L. If a sample of water has 150 mg/L of magnesium ions, what is its hardness in grains per gallon?

8.8 GPG

Classification of Water Hardness		
Classification	mg/L	GPG
Soft	0–60	0–3.5
Moderate	61–120	3.5–7
Hard	121–180	7–10.5
Very hard	> 180	> 10.5

Procedure

1. Use a grease pencil to label three large test tubes D (for distilled water), H (for hard water), and S (for soft water).

2. Use a 25-mL graduated cylinder to measure out 20-mL of distilled water. Pour the water into test tube D. Stopper the tube.

3. Place test tube H next to test tube D and make a mark on test tube H that corresponds to the height of the water in test tube D. Repeat the procedure with test tube S.

4. Obtain about 50-mL of hard water in a beaker from your teacher. Slowly pour hard water into test tube H until you reach the marked height.

5. Place a piece of filter paper on a balance and set

Analyze and Conclude

1. **Comparing and Contrasting** Which sample produced the most suds? Which sample produced the least suds? Set up your own water hardness scale based on your data. What is the relative hardness of the local water samples?

The test tube that contained the soft water had the largest volume of suds. The one with the hard water had the smallest volume. Answers will vary with local water.

CHEMLAB 7

2. **Using Numbers** The hard water you used was prepared by adding 1 gram of magnesium sulfate per liter of distilled water. Magnesium sulfate contains 20.2% magnesium ions by mass. What is its hardness in grains per gallon?

Hardness would be 2.0×10^2 mg/L or 12 GPG.

3. **Drawing a Conclusion** The compound in washing soda is sodium carbonate. How did the sodium carbonate soften the hard water?

Sodium carbonate combines with the magnesium sulfate in hard water to form an insoluble precipitate, which removes magnesium ions from the water.

4. **Thinking Critically** Remember that most compounds of alkaline earth metals do not dissolve easily in water. What is the white solid that formed when washing soda was added to the solution of magnesium sulfate?

The white solid is magnesium carbonate.

5. **Error Analysis** Could the procedure be changed to make the results more quantitative? Explain.

The volumes of the liquids and the detergent could be measured with more precision.

Real-World Chemistry

1. Water softeners for washing machines are sold in the detergent section of a store. Look at some of the packages and compare ingredients. Do packages that have different ingredients also have different instructions for how the water softener should be used?

yes

2. Suppose a family notices that the water pressure in their house is not good enough to flush a toilet on the second floor. Other than a leak, what could be interfering with the flow of water?

Hard-water deposits can form in pipes, causing corrosion and blocking the flow of water.

3. Explain why drinking hard water might be better for your health than drinking soft water. How could a family have the benefit of hard water for drinking and soft water for washing?

Calcium and magnesium ions are important minerals for health, so having some of these ions in water is beneficial; by adding water softeners to water used for washing

Name _____ Date _____ Class _____

CHEMLAB 8

Making Ionic Compounds

Elements combine to form compounds. If energy is released as the compound is formed, the resulting product is more stable than the reacting elements. In this investigation, you will react elements to form two compounds. You will test the compounds to determine several of their properties. Ionic compounds have properties that are different from those of other compounds. You will decide if the products you formed are ionic compounds.

Problem

What are the formulas and names of the products that are formed? Do the properties of these compounds classify them as having ionic bonds?

Objectives

- **Observe** evidence of a chemical reaction.
- **Acquire** and **analyze** information that will enable you to decide if a compound has an ionic bond.
- **Classify** the products as ionic or not ionic.

Materials

magnesium ribbon
crucible
ring stand and ring
clay triangle
laboratory burner
stirring rod
crucible tongs
centigram balance
100-mL beaker
distilled water
conductivity tester

Safety Precautions

- **Always wear safety glasses and a lab apron.**
- **Do not look directly at the burning magnesium. The intensity of the light can damage your eyes.**
- **Avoid handling heated materials until they have cooled.**

Pre-Lab

1. Read the entire CHEMLAB. Identify the variable. List any conditions that must be kept constant.
   Variable: mass of Mg; Constant: there must be an excess of oxygen

2. Write the electron configuration of the magnesium atom.
   Mg $1s^2 2s^2 2p^6 3s^2$
   a. Based on this configuration, will magnesium lose or gain electrons to become a magnesium ion?
   lose electrons
   b. Write the electron configuration of the magnesium ion.
   $Mg^{2+} 1s^2 2s^2 2p^6$
   c. The magnesium ion has an electron configuration like that of which noble gas?
   neon

3. Repeat question 2 for oxygen and nitrogen.
   O $1s^2 2s^2 2p^4$, N $1s^2 2s^2 2p^3$
   a. **Both will gain electrons.**
   b. **O^{2-} $1s^2 2s^2 2p^6$, N^{3-} $1s^2 2s^2 2p^6$**
   c. **Both have the configuration of neon.**

Name _____ Date _____ Class _____

miniLAB 8

Heat Treatment of Steel

Recognizing Cause and Effect People have treated metals with heat for many centuries. Different properties result when the metal is slowly or rapidly cooled. Can you determine how and why the properties change?

Materials laboratory burner, forceps (2), hairpins (3), 250-mL beaker

Procedure 🔥 🧤 🥽 ♻

1. Examine a property of spring steel by trying to bend open one of the hairpins. Record your observations.

2. Hold each end of a hairpin with forceps. Place the curved central loop in the top of the burner's flame. When it turns red, pull it open into a straight piece of metal. Allow it to cool as you record your observations. Repeat this procedure for the remaining two hairpins. **CAUTION:** *Do not touch the hot metal.*

3. To make softened steel, use forceps to hold all three hairpins vertically in the flame until they glow red all over. Slowly raise the three hairpins straight up and out of the flame so they cool slowly. Slow cooling results in the formation of large crystals.

4. After cooling, bend each of the three hairpins into the shape of the letter J. Record how the metal feels as you bend it.

5. To harden the steel, use tongs to hold two of the bent hairpins in the flame until they are glowing red all over. Quickly plunge the hot metals into a 250-mL beaker containing approximately 200 mL of cold water. Quick-cooling causes the crystal size to be small.

6. Attempt to straighten one of the bends. Record your observations.

7. To temper the steel, use tongs to briefly hold the remaining hardened metal bend above the flame. Slowly move the metal back and forth just above the flame until the gray metal turns to an iridescent blue-gray color. Do not allow the metal to glow red. Slowly cool the metal and then try to unbend it using the end of your finger. Record your observations.

Expected Results: **The metal can be straightened when heated because the layers of atoms separate and slide over one another easily. The hard steel breaks when students attempt to bend it. The tempered steel is hard and has a springlike feel.**

Analysis

1. State a use for spring steel that takes advantage of its unique properties.
   Answers may include pop-up tent, spring toys, and clips.

2. What are the advantages and disadvantages of using softened steel for body panels on automobiles?
   Smooth curves are possible, but they dent easily.

3. What is the major disadvantage of hardened steel? Do you think this form of iron would be wear resistant and retain a sharpened edge?
   brittle, breaks easily; yes

4. Which two types of steel appear to have their properties combined in tempered steel?
   spring and hardened steel

5. State a hypothesis that explains how the different properties you have observed relate to crystal size.
   Possible hypothesis: Soft steel has large crystals; hard steel has small crystals; tempered steel has intermediate-sized crystals.

CHEMLAB 8

4. Use the data table in the next column.

5. In your data table, which mass values will be measured directly? Which mass values will be calculated?

The mass of the magnesium and the mass of the magnesium products are calculated. Other mass values are measured directly.

6. Explain what must be done to calculate each mass value that is not measured directly.

The mass of magnesium ribbon is calculated by subtracting the mass of the crucible from the mass of the crucible and magnesium. The mass of the magnesium products is calculated by subtracting the mass of the crucible from the mass of the crucible and its contents after heating.

Procedure

1. Arrange the ring on the ring stand so that it is about 7 cm above the top of the Bunsen burner. Place the clay triangle on the ring.

2. Measure the mass of the clean, dry crucible, and record the mass in the data table.

3. Roll 25 cm of magnesium ribbon into a loose ball. Place it in the crucible. Measure the mass of the magnesium and crucible and record this mass in the data table.

4. Place the crucible on the clay ring. Heat the crucible with a hot flame, being careful to position the crucible near the top of the flame.

5. When the magnesium metal ignites and begins to burn with a bright white light, immediately turn off the laboratory burner. **CAUTION:** *Do not look directly at the burning magnesium.* After the magnesium product and crucible have cooled, measure their mass and record it in the data table.

6. Place the dry solid product in a small beaker for further testing.

7. Add 10 mL of distilled water to the dry magnesium product in the beaker and stir. Check the mixture with a conductivity checker, and record your results.

Sample Data

Mass Data	
Material(s)	Mass (g)
Empty crucible	7.65 g
Crucible and Mg ribbon before heating	7.85 g
Magnesium ribbon	0.20 g
Crucible and magnesium products after heating	7.93 g
Magnesium products	0.28 g

Cleanup and Disposal

1. Wash out the crucible with water.

2. Dispose of the product as directed by your teacher.

3. Return all lab equipment to its proper place.

Analyze and Conclude

1. **Analyzing Data** Use the masses in the table to calculate the mass of the magnesium ribbon and the mass of the magnesium product. Record these masses in the table.

2. **Classifying** What kind of energy was released by the reaction? What can you conclude about the product of this reaction?

Heat and light; it is more stable than the reacting elements.

CHEMLAB 8

3. **Using Numbers** How do you know that the magnesium metal reacts with certain components of the air?

There is an increase in mass from 0.20 g to 0.28 g.

4. **Predicting** Magnesium reacts with both oxygen and nitrogen from the air at the high temperature of the crucible. Predict the binary formulas for both products. Write the names of these two compounds.

MgO, magnesium oxide; Mg_3N_2, magnesium nitride

5. **Analyzing and Concluding** The product formed from magnesium and oxygen is white, and the product formed from magnesium and nitrogen is yellow. From your observations, which compound makes up most of the product?

MgO; the product appears white.

6. **Analyzing and Concluding** Did the magnesium compounds and water conduct an electric current? Do the results indicate whether or not the compounds are ionic?

Yes; ionic compounds conduct a current in solution.

7. **Error Analysis** If the magnesium lost mass instead of gaining mass, what do you think was a possible source of the error?

Possible answers include that some of the product blew away or that the reaction was incomplete.

Real-World Chemistry

1. The magnesium ion plays an important role in a person's biochemistry. Research the role of this electrolyte in your physical and mental health. Is magnesium listed as a component in a multivitamin and mineral tablet?

Answers may include that it is important in nerve impulse transmission. Mg is present in vitamin-mineral tablets.

2. Research the use of $Mg(OH)_2$ in everyday products. What is $Mg(OH)_2$ commonly called in over-the-counter drugs?

Answers might include that it is used in over-the-counter antacids and laxatives, where it is known as milk of magnesia.

CHEMLAB 9

Chromatography

Paper chromatography is a common way to separate various components of a mixture. The components of the mixture separate because different substances are selectively absorbed by paper due to differences in polarity. In this field or laboratory investigation, you will separate the various pigments found in leaves. You also will calculate the ratio called R_f for each of them. The ratio R_f compares the distance traveled by a substance, D_s, to the distance traveled by the solvent, D_f. The ratio is written as $R_f = D_s / D_f$.

Problem

How can a mixture be separated based on the polarity of substances in the mixture?

Objectives

- **Separate** pigments found in leaves.
- **Determine** the R_f value for each of the pigments in the leaves.

Materials

chromatography paper (3 pieces)
2-L plastic soft drink bottle
pencils (2)
metric ruler
tape
scissors or metal snips
aluminum foil
acetone
fresh leaf samples from three different species of deciduous trees or outdoor plants

Safety Precautions

- Acetone is a flammable liquid. Do not use near flames or sparks.
- Do not allow acetone to contact skin.
- Perform procedure in an area with proper ventilation.

Pre-Lab

1. Read the entire CHEMLAB.

2. Prepare all written materials that you will take into the laboratory. Be sure to include safety precautions and procedure notes. Use the data table on the next page to record your observations.

3. What is polarity? How is polarity related to how chromatography works?
   Polarity relates to an uneven distribution of charge. Because of differences in polarity, different materials will travel through a chromatographic medium at different rates because they are attracted to the medium differently.

4. Predict what will happen when a mixture of leaf pigments is placed on a piece of paper and a solvent is allowed to move through the paper, moving the pigment with it.
   Predictions might include that different components of the pigment mixture will separate and move at different rates.

---

miniLAB 9

Building VSEPR Models

Formulating Models The VSEPR model states that pairs of valence electrons on a central atom repel each other and are arranged so that the repulsions are as small as possible. In this **miniLAB**, you will use marshmallows and gumdrops to build models of substances, showing examples of the VSEPR model.

Materials regular-sized marshmallows (3); mini-sized marshmallows (9); small gumdrops (3); toothpicks, cut in half

Procedure

1. Draw Lewis structures for methane (CH_4), ammonia (NH_3), and water (H_2O). Notice the location of each shared and unshared pair of electrons.

2. Using your Lewis structures, build a VSEPR model for each molecule. Use a mini-marshmallow to represent both the hydrogen atom and the region of space containing the pair of electrons shared by hydrogen and the central atom. Use a regular-sized marshmallow to represent the space occupied by an unshared pair of electrons and a small gumdrop to represent a central atom. Use small pieces of toothpicks to attach the marshmallows and gumdrops to each other. Sketch each of your models.

Analysis

1. How did drawing a Lewis structure help you to determine the geometry of each of your substances?
   It serves as a guide to the approximate geometry of and bond angles in a molecule.

2. Why was a mini-marshmallow used to show a shared pair of electrons and a regular marshmallow an unshared pair?
   An unshared pair of electrons takes up more room in a molecule than does a shared pair.

3. How can the VSEPR model help to predict the bond angles for these substances?
   VSEPR shows how shared and unshared electron pairs arrange to reduce repulsions.

Expected Results: The lone pairs of electrons take up more space than paired electrons. Refer to Figure 9-3 to see Lewis structures for CH_4, NH_3, and H_2O. See Solutions Manual for sketches.

CHEMLAB 9

5. Suppose that the pigments in two samples contain red pigment and that the red pigment in sample A is more soluble in acetone than the red pigment in sample B. Form a hypothesis regarding which red pigment has the higher R_f value. Explain your answer.

Hypotheses might include that the more soluble pigment is probably more polar and its R_f will be greater because it will travel more closely to the speed of the solvent.

Procedure

1. For each leaf sample, crush the leaves and soak them in a small amount of acetone to make a concentrated solution of the pigments in the leaves.

2. Cut the top off a 2-liter bottle. Cut small notches, as shown in the figure so that a pencil can rest across the top of the bottle.

3. Cut three pieces of 3-cm wide chromatography paper to a length of about 18 cm. Label the top of each paper with a number. Assign a number to each pigment sample used. Draw pencil lines about 5 cm from the bottom of the end of each paper.

4. On the pencil line of paper 1, put a dot from the first sample. Make sure the dot is concentrated but not wide. Do the same for the other samples on their respective papers. Tape the papers to the pencil, as shown in the figure.

5. Put enough acetone in the 2-liter bottle so that when the papers are put in the bottle, the solvent touches only the bottom 1 cm of each paper, as shown in the figure. **CAUTION:** *Do not allow acetone to come in contact with skin. Use in area with proper ventilation.*

6. Carefully lower the chromatography papers into the acetone and put the pencil into the notches at the top of the bottle. Cover the top with aluminum foil. Allow the chromatograms to develop for about 35-40 minutes.

7. When the chromatograms are finished, remove them from the bottle. Mark the highest point reached by the solvent. Then, allow the papers to air dry.

Sample Data and Observations

Paper Chromatography				
Leaf sample	D_f (cm)	Colors	D_s (cm)	R_f
1	4.9	green	3.1	0.63
		yellow	3.9	0.80
		orange	4.8	0.98
		yellow	2.5	0.52
2	4.8	green	3.0	0.63
		orange	4.4	0.92
		yellow-orange	0.5	0.089
3	5.6	green	3.5	0.63
		orange	3.9	0.70

CHEMLAB 9

Cleanup and Disposal

1. Dispose of the acetone as directed by your teacher.

2. Throw the chromatography paper in the trash can.

Expected Results: Different components of the mixture would be expected to travel at different speeds. See the Data Table for sample results.

Analyze and Conclude

1. Observing and Inferring Record in the data table the colors that are found in each of the chromatograms. Space is allowed for three colors, but some samples may contain fewer or more than three colors.

2. Measuring For each strip, measure the distance the solvent traveled from the pencil line (D_f). For each color, measure from the top of the original marker dot to the farthest point the color traveled (D_s). Record these values in your data table.

3. Interpreting Data Calculate the R_f values for each of the pigments in each chromatogram and record them in the data table.

4. Comparing and Contrasting Describe the differences between the pigments in each of the samples.
Different colored pigments travel different distances. The pigments that have the greatest attraction to the paper don't travel as far.

5. Applying Concepts Will a polar solvent, such as water, cause a difference in how the pigments are separated? Explain your answer.
Polar components in the pigment mixture will be more attracted to water and will travel farther with it than nonpolar components will.

6. Error Analysis What could be done to improve the measurements you used to calculate R_f?
Answers might include having more than one person measuring D_s so all could be measured at the same time.

Real-World Chemistry

1. Use your results to explain what happens to leaves in autumn.
Answers might include that the pigments change in cold weather and those remaining are carried to different parts of the leaves based on polarity.

2. How might chromatography be used to analyze the composition of the dye in a marker?
Choose an appropriate solvent (water for a water-soluble marker and a nonpolar solvent for a permanent marker) and use a dot from the marker instead of a drop from the pigment mixture.

Copyright © Glencoe/McGraw-Hill, a division of the McGraw-Hill Companies, Inc.

miniLAB 10

Observing a Precipitate-Forming Reaction

Applying Concepts When two clear, colorless solutions are mixed, a chemical reaction may occur, resulting in the formation of a precipitate.

Materials 150-mL beakers (2); 100-mL graduated cylinder; stirring rod (2); spatula (2); weighing paper (2); NaOH; Epsom salts ($MgSO_4 \cdot 7H_2O$); distilled water; balance

Procedure

1. CAUTION: *Use gloves when working with NaOH.* Measure about 4 g NaOH and place it in a 150-mL beaker. Add 50 mL distilled water to the NaOH. Mix with a stirring rod until the NaOH dissolves.

2. Measure about 6 g Epsom salts and place it in another 150-mL beaker. Add 50 mL distilled water to the Epsom salts. Mix with another stirring rod until the Epsom salts dissolve.

3. Slowly pour the Epsom salts solution into the NaOH solution. Record your observations.

4. Stir the new solution. Record your observations.

5. Allow the precipitate to settle, then decant the liquid from the solid. Dispose of the solid as your teacher instructs.

Analysis

1. Write a chemical equation for the reaction between the NaOH and $MgSO_4$. Most sulfate compounds exist as ions in aqueous solutions.

$$MgSO_4(aq) + 2NaOH(aq) \rightarrow Mg(OH)_2(s) + Na_2SO_4(aq)$$

2. Write the complete ionic equation for this reaction.

$Mg^{2+}(aq) + SO_4^{2-}(aq) + 2Na^+(aq) + 2OH^-(aq) \rightarrow$

$Mg(OH)_2(s) + 2Na^+(aq) + SO_4^{2-}(aq)$

3. Write the net ionic equation for this reaction.

$Mg^{2+}(aq) + 2OH^-(aq) \rightarrow Mg(OH)_2(s)$

Expected Results: The reaction will form a white precipitate. When the precipitate is mixed, the solution resembles milk. The precipitate is magnesium hydroxide. Sodium and sulfate ions are not visible in the solution.

CHEMLAB 10

Activities of Metals

Some metals are more reactive than others. By comparing how different metals react with the same ions in aqueous solutions, an activity series for the tested metals can be developed. The activity series will reflect the relative reactivity of the tested metals. It can be used to predict whether reactions will occur.

Problem

Which is the most reactive metal tested? Which is the least reactive metal tested? Can this information be used to predict whether reactions will occur?

Objectives

• **Observe** chemical reactions.
• **Sequence** the activities of some metals.
• **Predict** if reactions will occur between certain substances.

Materials

1.0M $Zn(NO_3)_2$
1.0M $Al(NO_3)_3$
1.0M $Cu(NO_3)_2$
1.0M $Mg(NO_3)_2$
pipettes (4)
wire cutters
Cu wire

Al wire
Mg ribbon
Zn metal strips (4)
emery cloth or fine sandpaper
24-well microscale reaction plate

Safety Precautions

• Always wear safety goggles and a lab apron.
• Use caution when using sharp and coarse equipment.

Pre-Lab

1. Read the entire CHEMLAB.

2. Make notes about procedures and safety precautions to use in the laboratory.

3. Use the data table on the next page.

4. Form a hypothesis about what reactions will occur. **Answers may vary. Students should predict (a) that no reaction will occur when a metal is placed in an aqueous solution of a more reactive metal and (b) that a metal that is placed in an aqueous solution of a less reactive metal replaces the less reactive metal.**

5. What are the independent and dependent variables? **independent: solution concentration, amount of each type of metal, reaction time; dependent: reaction (no reaction), evidence of reaction, specific products of reaction**

6. What gas is produced when magnesium and hydrochloric acid react? Write the chemical equation for the reaction. **hydrogen; $Mg(s) + 2HCl(aq) \rightarrow MgCl_2(aq) + H_2(g)$**

CHEMLAB 10

7. Why is it important to clean the magnesium ribbon? How might not polishing a piece of metal affect the reaction involving that metal? **Oxidation or a coating on the metal may prevent it from making chemical contact with the solution.**

Procedure

1. Use a pipette to fill each of the four wells in column 1 of the reaction plate with 2 mL of 1.0M Al(NO₃)₃ solution.

2. Repeat the procedure in step 1 to fill the four wells in column 2 with 2 mL of 1.0M Mg(NO₃)₂ solution.

3. Repeat the procedure in step 1 to fill the four wells in column 3 with 2 mL of 1.0M Zn(NO₃)₂ solution.

4. Repeat the procedure in step 1 to fill the four wells in column 4 with 2 mL of 1.0M Cu(NO₃)₂ solution.

5. With the emery paper or sandpaper, polish 10 cm of aluminum wire until it is shiny. Use wire cutters to cut the aluminum wire into four 2.5-cm pieces. Place a piece of the aluminum wire in each row A well that contains solution.

6. Repeat the procedure in step 5 using 10 cm of magnesium ribbon. Place a piece of the Mg ribbon in each row B well that contains solution.

7. Use the emery paper or sandpaper to polish small strips of zinc metal. Place a piece of Zn metal in each row C well that contains solution.

8. Repeat the procedure in step 5 using 10 cm of copper wire. Place a piece of Cu wire in each row D well that contains solution.

9. Observe what happens in each cell. After 5 minutes, record your observations in the data table.

Reactions Between Solutions and Metals

	Al(NO₃)₃	Mg(NO₃)₂	Zn(NO₃)₂	Cu(NO₃)₂
Al	No	No	Yes	Yes
Mg	Yes	No	Yes	Yes
Zn	No	No	No	Yes
Cu	No	No	No	No

Cleanup and Disposal

1. Dispose of all chemicals and solutions as directed by your teacher.

2. Clean your equipment and return it to its proper place.

3. Wash your hands thoroughly before you leave the lab.

Analyze and Conclude

1. **Observing and Inferring** In which wells of the reaction plate did chemical reactions occur? Which metal reacted with the most solutions? Which metal reacted with the fewest solutions? Which metal is the most reactive? **A3, A4, B1, B3, B4, C4; Mg—3 reactions; Cu—0 reactions; Magnesium is the most reactive.**

2. **Sequencing** The most active metal reacted with the most solutions. The least active metal reacted with the fewest solutions. Order the four metals from the most active to the least active. **Mg, Al, Zn, Cu**

CHEMLAB 10

3. **Comparing and Contrasting** Compare your activity series with the activity series shown here. How does the order you determined for the four metals you tested compare with the order of these metals? **The order is the same.**

METALS
Most active ⟶
Lithium
Rubidium
Potassium
Calcium
Sodium
Magnesium
Aluminum
Manganese
Zinc
Iron
Nickel
Tin
Lead
Copper
Silver
Platinum
Gold
Least active

HALOGENS
Most active ⟶
Fluorine
Chlorine
Bromine
Iodine
Least active

4. **Applying Concepts** Write a chemical equation for each single-replacement reaction that occurred on your reaction plate.

A3: 2Al(s) + 3Zn(NO₃)₂(aq) → 2Al(NO₃)₃(aq) + 3Zn(s)

A4: 2Al(s) + 3Cu(NO₃)₂(aq) → 2Al(NO₃)₃(aq) + 3Cu(s)

B1: 3Mg(s) + 2Al(NO₃)₃(aq) → 3Mg(NO₃)₂(aq) + 2Al(s)

B3: Mg(s) + Zn(NO₃)₂(aq) → Mg(NO₃)₂(aq) + Zn(s)

B4: Mg(s) + Cu(NO₃)₂(aq) → Mg(NO₃)₂(aq) + Cu(s)

C4: Zn(s) + Cu(NO₃)₂(aq) → Zn(NO₃)₂(aq) + Cu(s)

5. **Predicting** Use the diagram to predict if a single-replacement reaction will occur between the following reactants. Write a chemical equation for each reaction that will occur.

a. Ca and Sn(NO₃)₂   **yes, Ca(s) + Sn(NO₃)₂(aq) → Ca(NO₃)₂(aq) + Sn(s)**

b. Ag and Ni(NO₃)₂   **no**

c. Cu and Pb(NO₃)₃   **no**

6. **Error Analysis** If the activity series you sequenced does not agree with the order in the diagram above, propose a reason for the disagreement. **Answers may vary. If the procedure was not followed or if the contents of two wells mixed due to overfilling, then the activity series would not agree.**

Real-World Chemistry

1. Under what circumstances might it be important to know the activity tendencies of a series of elements? **Answers may vary. For example, industrial chemists could use the information to fine-tune a product or process.**

2. Describe some of the environmental impacts of nitrates. **Answers may vary. For example, students may discuss nitrates as fertilizers or the dangers of nitrates in water supplies. They may also describe nitrate removal procedures.**

miniLAB 11

Percent Composition and Gum

Interpreting Data Water soluble sweeteners and flavorings are added to chewing gum. Are these chemicals added as an outside coating or are they mixed throughout the gum?

Materials balance, weighing paper, 250-mL beakers (2), pieces of chewing gum (2), stirring rod, paper towels, window screen (10 cm × 10 cm), scissors, clock or timer

Procedure

CAUTION: *Do not taste or eat any items used in the lab.*

1. Unwrap two pieces of chewing gum. Measure the mass of each separately on a piece of weighing paper. Label the weighing papers with the masses to avoid mixing up your data. Record the masses.

2. Add 150 mL of cold tap water to a 250-mL beaker. Place one piece of chewing gum in the water and stir for 2 minutes.

3. Remove the gum from the water and pat dry using paper towels. Measure and record the mass of the dried gum.

4. Use scissors to cut the second piece of gum into small pieces, each about the width of a pea. Repeat step 2 using fresh water. Use the stirring rod to keep the pieces of gum from clumping together.

5. Use the window screen to strain the water from the gum. Pat the gum dry using paper towels. Measure and record the mass of the dried gum.

6. Discard the gum in a waste container.

Expected Results:
The gum will lose mass after being placed in water because the sweeteners are water-soluble. The cut piece with the larger surface area will expose more of the soluble chemicals to the water, and will have a greater loss of mass.

Analysis

1. For the uncut piece of gum, calculate the mass of sweeteners and flavorings that dissolved in the water. The mass of sweeteners and flavorings is the difference between the original mass of the gum and the mass of the dried gum.

   (initial mass) − (final mass) = 3.11 g − 2.84 g = 0.27 g dissolved sweeteners and flavorings

2. For the gum that was in small pieces, calculate the mass of dissolved sweeteners and flavorings.

   (initial mass) − (final mass) = 3.11 g − 2.75 g = 0.36 g dissolved sweeteners and flavorings

3. For both pieces of gum, calculate the percent of the original mass that was soluble sweeteners and flavorings. For help, refer to *Percents* in the **Math Handbook** on page 909 of your textbook.

   whole piece of gum: 0.27 g/3.11 g × 100 = 8.7%

   small pieces of gum: 0.36 g/3.11 g × 100 = 12%

4. What can you infer from the two percentages? Is the gum sugar-coated or are the sweeteners and flavorings mixed throughout?

   Because more sweetener dissolves when the surface area is larger, the inference is that the sweeteners are mixed throughout the gum.

CHEMLAB 11

Hydrated Crystals

Hydrates are compounds that incorporate water molecules in their crystalline structures. The ratio of moles of water to one mole of the compound is a small whole number. For example, in the hydrated compound copper(II) sulfate pentahydrate ($CuSO_4 \cdot 5H_2O$), the ratio is 5:1. The ratio of moles of water to one mole of a hydrate can be determined experimentally by heating the hydrate to remove water.

Problem

How can you determine the moles of water in a mole of a hydrated compound?

Objectives

- **Heat** a known mass of hydrated compound until the water is removed.
- **Calculate** the formula for a hydrate using the mass of the hydrated compound and the mass of the anhydrous compound.

Materials

Bunsen burner
ring stand and ring
crucible and lid
clay triangle
crucible tongs
balance
Epsom salts (hydrated $MgSO_4$)
spatula
spark lighter or matches

Safety Precautions

- Always wear safety goggles and a lab apron.
- Hot objects will not appear to be hot.
- Use the Bunsen burner carefully.
- Turn off the Bunsen burner when not in use.

Pre-Lab

1. Read the entire CHEMLAB.

2. Prepare all written materials that you will take into the laboratory. Be sure to include safety precautions and procedure notes. Use the data table on the next page.

3. Explain how you will obtain the mass of water and the mass of anhydrous $MgSO_4$ contained in the hydrate.
   To obtain the mass of water, subtract the mass of the crucible, cover, and anhydrous $MgSO_4$ from the mass of the crucible, cover, and hydrated $MgSO_4$. To obtain the mass of anhydrous $MgSO_4$, subtract the mass of the crucible and cover from the mass of the crucible, cover, and anhydrous $MgSO_4$.

4. How will you convert the masses of anhydrous $MgSO_4$ and water to moles?
   Divide by the molar mass.

5. How can you obtain the formula for the hydrate from the moles of anhydrous $MgSO_4$ and the moles of water?
   Calculate the ratio of moles of water to moles of anhydrous $MgSO_4$.

CHEMLAB 11

Sample Data

Mass Data and Observations of Epsom Salts

Observations of hydrated $MgSO_4$	Shiny, translucent crystals
Mass of crucible and lid	11.36 g
Mass of crucible, lid, and hydrated $MgSO_4$	14.36 g
Mass of hydrated $MgSO_4$	3.00 g
Mass of crucible, lid, and anhydrous $MgSO_4$	12.83 g
Mass of anhydrous $MgSO_4$	1.47 g
Mass of water in hydrated $MgSO_4$	1.53 g
Moles of anhydrous $MgSO_4$	0.0122 mol
Moles of water in hydrated $MgSO_4$	0.0849 mol
Observation of anhydrous $MgSO_4$	Bright white, opaque, powdery

Procedure

1. Measure to the nearest 0.01 g the mass of a clean, dry crucible with a lid. Record the mass.
2. Add about 3 g hydrated $MgSO_4$ to the crucible. Measure the mass of the crucible, lid, and hydrate to the nearest 0.01 g and record the mass.
3. Record your observations of the hydrate.
4. Place the triangle on the ring of the ring stand. Carefully place the crucible in the triangle.
5. Place the crucible lid on the crucible slightly cocked to help prevent spattering and allow vapor to escape. Begin heating with a low flame, then gradually progress to a stronger flame. Heat for about 10 minutes.
6. When heating is complete, remove the crucible using tongs. Place the lid on the crucible and allow the crucible and contents to cool.
7. Measure the mass of the crucible, lid, and $MgSO_4$ and record the mass in the data table.
8. Observe the anhydrous $MgSO_4$ and record your observations.

Cleanup and Disposal

1. Discard the anhydrous $MgSO_4$ in a trash container or as directed by your teacher.
2. Return all lab equipment to its proper place and clean your lab station.
3. Wash your hands thoroughly when all lab work and cleanup are complete.

CHEMLAB 11

Analyze and Conclude

1. **Using Numbers** Use your experimental data to calculate the formula for hydrated $MgSO_4$.

   Calculation of mole ratio: Moles of $MgSO_4$ = 1.47 g × 1 mol/120.4 g = 0.0122 mol $MgSO_4$

   Moles of water = 1.53 g × 1 mol/18.02 g = 0.0849 mol water

   Mole ratio = 0.0849 mol H_2O/0.0122 mol $MgSO_4$ = 6.96 or approximately 7

   The formula is $MgSO_4 \cdot 7H_2O$.

2. **Observing and Inferring** How did your observations of the hydrated $MgSO_4$ crystals compare with those of the anhydrous $MgSO_4$ crystals?
   The hydrated $MgSO_4$ is shiny and translucent. The anhydrous $MgSO_4$ is opaque and bright white.

3. **Drawing Conclusions** Why might the method used in this experiment not be suitable for determining the water of hydration for all hydrates?
   Some hydrates may decompose when heated.

4. **Error Analysis** What is the percent error of your calculation of the water of hydration for $MgSO_4$ if the formula for the hydrate is $MgSO_4 \cdot 7H_2O$? What changes would you make in the procedure to reduce error?
   Answers will vary. (7.00 − 6.96)/7.00 × 100 = 0.57% error

   Students may suggest longer heating and guarding against loss of salt by spattering.

5. **Predicting** What might you observe if the anhydrous crystals were left uncovered overnight?
   The anhydrous $MgSO_4$ may absorb water.

Real-World Chemistry

1. Packets of the anhydrous form of a hydrate are sometimes used to keep cellars from being damp. Is there a limit to how long a packet could be used?
   Yes, eventually, the anhydrous compound will absorb as much water as is possible and can no longer act as a desiccant.

2. Gypsum ($CaSO_4 \cdot 2H_2O$) is a mineral used for making wallboard for construction. The mineral is stripped of three-quarters of its water of hydration in a process called calcining. Then, after mixing with water, it hardens to a white substance called plaster of paris. Infer what happens as calcined gypsum becomes plaster of paris.
   The addition of water causes the anhydrous compound to become hydrated.

miniLAB 12
Baking Soda Stoichiometry

Predicting When baking soda is an ingredient in your recipe, its purpose is to make the batter rise and produce a product with a light and fluffy texture. That's because baking soda, or sodium hydrogen carbonate ($NaHCO_3$), decomposes upon heating to form carbon dioxide gas.

$$2NaHCO_3 \rightarrow Na_2CO_3 + CO_2 + H_2O$$

Predict how much sodium carbonate (Na_2CO_3) is produced when baking soda decomposes.

Materials ring stand, ring, clay triangle, crucible, crucible tongs, Bunsen burner, balance, 3.0 g baking soda ($NaHCO_3$)

Procedure

1. Measure the mass of a clean, dry crucible. Add about 3.0 g of $NaHCO_3$ and measure the combined mass of the crucible and $NaHCO_3$. Record both masses and calculate the mass of the $NaHCO_3$.

_____

2. Use this starting mass of baking soda and the balanced chemical equation to calculate the mass of Na_2CO_3 that will be produced.

_____

3. Set up a ring stand with a ring and clay triangle for heating the crucible.

4. Heat the crucible slowly at first and then with a stronger flame for 7–8 min. Use tongs to remove the hot crucible. Record your observations during the heating.

5. Allow the crucible to cool and then obtain the mass of the crucible and sodium carbonate.

Analysis

1. What were your observations during the heating of the baking soda? **During heating, the product started looking "wet" and bubbles appeared. In time, the product "dried out."**

_____

2. How did your calculated mass of sodium carbonate compare with the actual mass you obtained from the experiment? If the two masses are different, suggest reasons for the difference. **Percent yield = (1.90 g/1.97 g) × 100 = 96.4% Calculated and actual masses should be similar. Experimental error could explain a difference.**

Expected Results: A mass of 3.12 g baking soda may yield approximately 1.90 g Na_2CO_3.

CHEMLAB 12
A Mole Ratio

Iron reacts with copper(II) sulfate in a single replacement reaction. By measuring the mass of iron that reacts and the mass of copper metal produced, you can calculate the ratio of moles of reactant to moles of product. This mole ratio can be compared to the ratio found in the balanced chemical equation.

Problem

Which reactant is the limiting reactant? How does the experimental mole ratio of Fe to Cu compare with the mole ratio in the balanced chemical equation? What is the percent yield?

Objectives

- **Observe** a single replacement reaction.
- **Measure** the masses of iron and copper.
- **Calculate** the moles of each metal and the mole ratio.

Materials

iron metal filings, 20 mesh
copper(II) sulfate pentahydrate ($CuSO_4 \cdot 5H_2O$)
distilled water
stirring rod
150-mL beaker
400-mL beaker
100-mL graduated cylinder
weighing paper
balance
hot plate
beaker tongs

Safety Precautions

- Always wear safety glasses and a lab apron.
- Hot objects will not appear to be hot.
- Do not heat broken, chipped, or cracked glassware.
- Turn off the hot plate when not in use.

Pre-Lab

1. Read the entire **CHEMLAB**.

2. Prepare all written materials that you will take into the laboratory. Be sure to include safety precautions and procedure notes. Use the data table on the next page.

3. Is it important that you know you are using the hydrated form of copper(II) sulfate? Would it be possible to use the anhydrous form? Why or why not? **It is not important to use hydrated copper(II) sulfate rather than anhydrous copper(II) sulfate because, in this experiment, iron is the limiting reactant. As long as the number of moles of copper sulfate exceeds the number of moles of iron (ratio of Cu^{2+} to Fe is 1:1), either form of the compound could be used.**

Procedure

1. Measure and record the mass of a clean, dry 150-mL beaker.

2. Place approximately 12 g of copper(II) sulfate pentahydrate into the 150-mL beaker and measure and record the combined mass.

3. Add 50 mL of distilled water to the copper(II) sulfate pentahydrate and heat the mixture on the hot plate at a medium setting. Stir until all of the solid is dissolved, but do not boil. Using tongs, remove the beaker from the hot plate.

4. Measure approximately 2 g of iron metal filings onto a piece of weighing paper. Measure and record the exact mass of the filings.

5. While stirring, slowly add the iron filings to the hot copper(II) sulfate solution.

6. Allow the reaction mixture to stand, without stirring, for 5 minutes to ensure complete reaction. The solid copper metal will settle to the bottom of the beaker.

CHEMLAB 12

7. Use the stirring rod to decant (pour off) the liquid into a 400-mL beaker. Be careful to decant only the liquid.

8. Add 15 mL of distilled water to the copper solid and carefully swirl the beaker to wash the copper. Decant the liquid into the 400-mL beaker.

9. Repeat step 8 two more times.

10. Place the 150-mL beaker containing the wet copper on the hot plate. Use low heat to dry the copper.

11. Remove the beaker from the hot plate and allow it to cool.

12. Measure and record the mass of the cooled 150-mL beaker and the copper.

Cleanup and Disposal

1. Make sure the hot plate is off.
2. The dry copper can be placed in a waste container. Wet any residue that sticks to the beaker and wipe it out using a paper towel. Pour the unreacted copper(II) sulfate and iron(II) sulfate solutions into a large beaker in the fume hood.
3. Return all lab equipment to its proper place.
4. Wash your hands thoroughly after all lab work and cleanup is complete.

Data for the Reaction of Copper(II) Sulfate and Iron	
Mass of empty 150-mL beaker	69.87 g
Mass of 150-mL beaker + $CuSO_4 \cdot 5H_2O$	81.92 g
Mass of $CuSO_4 \cdot 5H_2O$	12.05 g
Mass of iron filings	2.02 g
Mass of 150-mL beaker and dried copper	72.13 g
Mass of dried copper	2.26 g
Observations	

Analyze and Conclude

1. **Observing and Inferring** What evidence did you observe that confirms that a chemical reaction occurred?
The solution changed color and the copper precipitated.

2. **Applying Concepts** Write a balanced chemical equation for the single-replacement reaction that occurred.
$Fe(s) + CuSO_4(aq) \rightarrow Cu(s) + FeSO_4(aq)$

3. **Interpreting Data** From your data, determine the mass of copper produced.
72.13 g − 69.87 g = 2.26 g Cu

4. **Using Numbers** Use the mass of copper to calculate the moles of copper produced.
2.26 g Cu × 1 mol Cu/63.55 g Cu = 0.0356 mol Cu

CHEMLAB 12

5. **Using Numbers** Calculate the moles of iron used in the reaction.
2.02 g Fe × 1 mol Fe/55.85 g Fe = 0.0362 mol Fe

6. **Using Numbers** Determine the whole number ratio of moles of iron to moles of copper.
mol Fe/mole Cu = 0.0362/0.0356 = 1.02

7. **Comparing and Contrasting** Compare the ratio of moles of iron to moles of copper from the balanced chemical equation to the mole ratio calculated using your data.
The ratio of Fe to Cu in the equation is 1:1, almost the same as the experimental ratio.

8. **Evaluating Results** Use the balanced chemical equation to calculate the mass of copper that should have been produced from the sample of iron you used. Use this number and the mass of copper you actually obtained to calculate the percent yield.
0.0362 mol Fe × 1 mol Cu/1 mol Fe × 63.55 g/1 mol Cu = 2.30 g Cu
Percent yield = 2.26 g/2.30 g × 100 = 98.3%

9. **Error Analysis** What was the source of any deviation from the mole ratio calculated from the chemical equation? How could you improve your results?
The copper was not completely dry. Some copper could have oxidized if heated too hot. Copper also could have been lost. Use lower heat for a longer time. Use extra care in decanting.

10. **Drawing a Conclusion** Which reactant is the limiting reactant? Explain.
Iron is the limiting reactant. All the iron was used up.

Real-World Chemistry

1. A furnace that provides heat by burning methane gas (CH_4) must have the correct mixture of air and fuel to operate efficiently. What is the mole ratio of air to methane gas in the combustion of methane? Hint: Air is 20% oxygen.
$CH_4 + 2O_2 \rightarrow CO_2 + 2H_2O$
1 mole of methane requires 2 moles of pure oxygen or 10 moles of air (20% O_2).
This ratio shows that a large volume of air goes up the chimney.

2. Automobile air bags inflate on impact because a series of gas-producing chemical reactions are triggered. To be effective in saving lives, the bags must not overinflate or underinflate. What factors must automotive engineers take into account in the design of air bags?
Automotive engineers must take into account the size of the bag and the amounts of the reactants. Just the right amount of product must form to inflate the bag but not overinflate it.

Name _____ Date _____ Class _____

miniLAB 13
Crystal Unit Cell Models

Formulating Models You can make physical models that illustrate the structures of crystals.

Materials plastic or paper soda straws (12), 22- or 26-gauge wire, scissors

Procedure

1. Cut four soda straws into thirds. Wire the pieces to make a cube. All angles are 90°.
2. To model a rhombohedral crystal, deform the cube from step 1 until no angles are 90°.
3. To model a hexagonal crystal, flatten the model from step 2 until it looks like a pie with six slices.
4. To model a tetragonal crystal, cut four straws in half. Cut four of the pieces in half again. Wire the eight shorter pieces to make four square ends. Use the longer pieces to connect the square ends.
5. To model the orthorhombic crystal, cut four straws in half. Cut 1/3 off four of the halves. Connect the four long, four medium, and four short pieces so that each side is a rectangle.
6. To model the monoclinic crystal, deform the model from step 5 along one axis. To model the triclinic crystal, deform the model from step 5 until it has no 90° angles.

Analysis

1. Which two models have three axes of equal length? How do these models differ?
The two crystal models that have all three axes of equal length are cubic and rhombohedral. They differ in that the cubic model has only 90-degree angles; the rhombohedral model has no 90-degree angles.

2. Which model includes a square and rectangle?
the tetragonal crystal model

3. Which models have three unequal axes?
The three crystal models that have three axes of unequal length are orthorhombic, monoclinic, and triclinic.

4. Do you think crystals are perfect or do they have defects? Explain your answer.
They are not perfectly uniform, as they can be affected by external forces and conditions.

Expected Results: Students will construct the seven unit cells shown in Figures 13–19.

Name _____ Date _____ Class _____

CHEMLAB 13

Comparing Rates of Evaporation

Several factors determine how fast a sample of liquid will evaporate. The volume of the sample is a key factor. A drop of water takes less time to evaporate than a liter of water. The amount of energy supplied to the sample is another factor. In this lab, you will investigate how the type of liquid and temperature affect the rate of evaporation.

Problem

How do intermolecular forces affect the evaporation rates of liquids?

Objectives

* **Measure** and **compare** the rates of evaporation for different liquids.
* **Classify** liquids based on their rates of evaporation.
* **Predict** which intermolecular forces exist between the particles of each liquid.

Materials

distilled water
ethanol
isopropyl alcohol
acetone
household ammonia
droppers (5)
small plastic cups (5)
grease pencil or masking tape and a marking pen
paper towel
square of waxed paper
stopwatch

Safety Precautions

* Always wear safety goggles and a lab apron.
* Wear gloves because some of the liquids can dry out your skin.
* Avoid inhaling any of the vapors, especially ammonia.
* There should be no open flames in the lab; some of the liquids are flammable.

Pre-Lab

1. Read the entire CHEMLAB. Use the data table on the next page.

2. What is evaporation? Describe what happens at the molecular level during evaporation.
Evaporation is the process by which molecules at the surface of a liquid change to a gas or a vapor. As liquid molecules acquire kinetic energy, they reach the minimum required energy to overcome the forces of attraction holding them together.

3. List the three possible intermolecular forces. Which force is the weakest? Which force is the strongest?
dispersion forces, dipole-dipole forces, hydrogen bonds; weakest: dispersion forces; strongest: hydrogen bonds.

4. Look at the materials list for this lab. Consider the five liquids you will test. Predict which liquids will evaporate quickly and which will take longer to evaporate. Give reasons for your predictions.
Students should predict that organic liquids will evaporate more quickly than H_2O or NH_3 because there are fewer forces between the particles of liquid.

CHEMLAB 13

5. To calculate an evaporation rate, you would divide the evaporation time by the quantity of liquid used. Explain why it is possible to use the evaporation times from this lab as evaporation rates.

Evaporation times can be used as rates because the same quantity (a drop) was used for each liquid.

6. Make sure you know how to use the stopwatch provided. Will you need to convert the reading on the stopwatch to seconds?

Procedure

1. Use a grease pencil or masking tape to label each of five small plastic cups. Use A for distilled water, B for ethanol, C for isopropyl alcohol, D for acetone, and E for household ammonia.
2. Place the plastic cups on a paper towel.
3. Use a dropper to collect about 1 mL of distilled water and place the water in the cup labeled A. Place the dropper on the paper towel directly in front of the cup. Repeat with the other liquids.
4. Place a square of waxed paper on your lab surface. Plan where on the waxed paper you will place each of the 5 drops that you will test. The drops must be as far apart as possible to avoid mixing.
5. Have your stopwatch ready. Collect some water in your water dropper and place a single drop on the waxed paper. Begin timing. Time how long it takes for the drop to completely evaporate. While you wait, make two drawings of the drop. One drawing should show the shape of the drop as viewed from above. The other drawing should be a side view at eye level. If the drop takes longer than 5 minutes to evaporate, record > 300 in your data table.
6. Repeat step 5 with the four other liquids.
7. Use the above procedure to design an experiment in which you can observe the effect of temperature on the rate of evaporation of ethanol. Your teacher will provide a sample of warm ethanol. Record your observations.

Cleanup and Disposal

1. Crumple up the waxed paper and place it in the container assigned by your teacher.
2. Place unused liquids in the containers specified by your teacher.
3. Wash out all droppers and test tubes except those used for distilled water.

Evaporation Data

Liquid	Evaporation time (s)	Shape of liquid drop
Distilled water	> 300	Top: spherical; Side: domed
Ethanol	140	Top: jagged circular; Side: flat
Ethanol (warm)	< 140	Top: jagged circular; Side: flat
Isopropyl alcohol	146	Same as ethanol
Acetone	8.4	Top: small circular; Side: flat
Household ammonia	> 300	Same as water

Analyze and Conclude

1. **Classifying** Which liquids evaporated quickly? Which liquids were slow to evaporate?

Acetone evaporates the fastest; the water and ammonia evaporate the slowest.

CHEMLAB 13

2. **Drawing a Conclusion** Based on your data, in which liquid(s) are the attractive forces between molecules most likely to be dispersion forces?

in the liquid that is nonpolar and that evaporates the fastest (acetone)

3. **Interpreting Data** Make a generalization about the shape of a liquid drop and the evaporation rate of the liquid.

See the Solutions Manual.

4. **Recognizing Cause and Effect** What is the relationship between surface tension and the shape of a liquid drop? What are the attractive forces that increase surface tension?

See the Solutions Manual.

5. **Applying Concepts** The isopropyl alcohol you used is a mixture of isopropyl alcohol and water. Would pure isopropyl alcohol evaporate more quickly or more slowly compared to the alcohol and water mixture? Give a reason for your answer.

See the Solutions Manual.

6. **Thinking Critically** Household ammonia is a mixture of ammonia and water. Based on the data you collected, is there more ammonia or more water in the mixture? Use what you learned about the relative strengths of the attractive forces in ammonia and water to support your conclusion.

See the Solutions Manual.

7. **Drawing a Conclusion** How does the rate of evaporation of warm ethanol compare to ethanol at room temperature? Use kinetic-molecular theory to explain your observations.

See the Solutions Manual.

8. **Error Analysis** How could you change the procedure to make it more precise?

by determining the exact volume of each liquid tested

Real-World Chemistry

1. The vapor phases of liquids such as acetone and alcohol are more flammable than their liquid phases. For flammable liquids, what is the relationship between evaporation rate and the likelihood that the liquid will burn?

The higher the evaporation rate, the more likely the liquid will burn.

2. Suggest why a person who has a higher than normal temperature might be given a rubdown with rubbing alcohol (70% isopropyl alcohol).

See the Solutions Manual.

3. Table salt can be collected from salt water by evaporation. The water is placed in large, shallow containers. What advantage do these shallow containers have over deep containers with the same overall volume?

They provide greater surface area for evaporation.

Name _____ Date _____ Class _____

miniLAB 14
The Density of Carbon Dioxide

Hypothesizing Air is a mixture of mostly nitrogen and oxygen. Use observations to form a hypothesis about which has greater density, air or carbon dioxide.

Materials masking tape, aluminum foil, metric ruler, 1-L beaker, candle, matches, thermometer, barometer or weather radio, baking soda ($NaHCO_3$), vinegar (5% CH_3COOH)

Procedure

1. Record the temperature and the barometric pressure of the air in the classroom.
2. Roll a 23-cm × 30-cm piece of aluminum foil into a cylinder that is 6 cm × 30 cm. Tape the edges with masking tape.
3. Use matches to light a candle. **CAUTION:** *Run water over the extinguished match before throwing it away. Keep all hair and loose clothing away from the flame.*
4. Place 30 g of baking soda in the bottom of a large beaker. Add 40 mL of vinegar.
5. Quickly position the foil cylinder at approximately 45° up and away from the top of the candle flame.
6. While the reaction in the beaker is actively producing CO_2 gas, carefully pour the gas, but not the liquid, out of the beaker and into the top of the foil tube. Record your observations.

Analysis

1. Based on your observations, state a hypothesis about whether CO_2 is heavier or lighter than air.
   CO_2 gas is heavier than air.

2. Use the combined gas law to calculate molar volume at room temperature and atmospheric pressure.
   Using $V_2 = P_1V_1T_2/(T_1P_2)$ at 298 K and 98.6 kPa, the molar volume is 25.1 L.

3. Carbon dioxide gas (CO_2) has a molar mass of 44 g/mol. The two major components of air, which are oxygen and nitrogen, have molar masses of 32 g/mol and 28 g/mol, respectively. Calculate the room-temperature densities in g/L of nitrogen (N_2), oxygen (O_2), and carbon dioxide (CO_2) gases.
   N_2 28.0 g/25.1 L = 1.12 g/L; O_2 32.0 g/25.1 L = 1.27 g/L; CO_2 44.0 g/25.1 L = 1.75 g/L

4. Do these calculations confirm your hypothesis? Explain.
   Yes, the heavier CO_2 gas moves down the cylinder, displacing the air and extinguishing the candle flame.

Expected Results: The heavier-than-air CO_2 gas will flow down the foil cylinder and extinguish the candle flame.

Name _____ Date _____ Class _____

CHEMLAB 14

Using the Ideal Gas Law

The ideal gas law is a powerful tool that the chemist—and now you—can use to determine the molar mass of an unknown gas. By measuring the temperature, pressure, volume, and mass of a gas sample, you can calculate the molar mass of the gas.

Problem
How can the equation for the ideal gas law be used to calculate the molar mass of a gas?

Objectives
- **Measure** the mass, volume, temperature, and pressure of an insoluble gas collected over water.
- **Calculate** the molar mass of an unknown gas using the ideal gas equation.

Materials
aerosol can of duster
600-mL graduated beaker
bucket or bowl
thermometer (°C)
barometer or weather radio
plastic microtip pipette
latex tubing
glass tubing
scissors
electrical or duct tape
balance

Safety Precautions

- **Read and observe all cautions listed on the aerosol can of office equipment duster.**
- **Do not have any open flames in the room.**

Pre-Lab

1. Read the entire CHEMLAB.
2. Prepare all written materials that you will take into the laboratory. Be sure to include safety precautions and procedure notes. Use the data table on the next page.
3. Because you will collect the aerosol gas over water, the beaker contains both the aerosol gas and water vapor. Form a hypothesis about how the presence of water vapor will affect the calculated value of the molar mass of the gas. Explain.
   Because the molar mass of water is likely to be less than that of the other gas present, it probably will lower the calculated molar mass of the other gas.

4. The following gases are or have been used in aerosol cans, some as propellants. Use the gases' molecular formulas to calculate their molar masses.
   a. propane, C_3H_8
      44.11 g/mol
   b. butane, C_4H_{10}
      58.14 g/mol
   c. dichlorodifluoromethane, CCl_2F_2
      120.91 g/mol
   d. tetrafluoroethane, $C_2H_2F_4$
      102.04 g/mol

5. Given the following data for a gas, use the equation for the ideal gas law to calculate the molar mass.
   a. mass = 0.810 g
   b. pressure = 0.954 atm
   c. volume = 0.461 L
   d. temperature = 291 K
   $M = mRT/PV = 0.810\ g \times 0.0821$ L·atm/ (mol·K) $\times 291$ K/(0.954 atm $\times 0.461$ L) $= 44.0$ g/mol

CHEMLAB 14

Procedure

1. Place the bucket in the sink and fill it with water.
2. Submerge the beaker in the water. Then, invert it in the bucket, being careful to keep it completely filled with water.
3. Measure the mass of an aerosol can of office equipment duster. Record the mass in the data table.
4. Use scissors to cut the stem from a plastic microtip pipette.
5. Fit the pipette stem over the long plastic spray tip that comes with the aerosol can to extend the length of the tip and enlarge the diameter.
6. Connect one end of 30 cm of latex tubing to glass tubing that is 8 cm long.
7. Connect the other end to the pipette stem that is attached to the aerosol can. If necessary, tape any connections so that they don't leak.
8. Place the end of the glass tubing under the pour spout of the inverted beaker.
9. Hold the beaker down while you slowly release the gas from the aerosol can. Collect between 400 and 500 mL of the gas by water displacement.
10. To equalize the air pressure, lift the beaker so that the water level inside and outside the beaker is the same.
11. Carefully read the volume of the gas collected using the graduations on the beaker.
12. Record this volume of the gas collected in the data table.

13. Remove the tubing from the aerosol can.
14. Measure the mass of the can and record it in the data table.
15. Using a barometer or weather radio, record the atmospheric pressure in the data table.
16. Using a thermometer, determine air temperature. Record it in the data table.

Sample Data

Data and Calculations	
Mass of can before release of gas (g)	265.0 g
Mass of can after release of gas (g)	262.9 g
Mass of gas released (g)	2.1 g
Air temperature (°C)	25°C
Air temperature (K)	298 K
Air pressure (list what unit was used)	760 mm Hg
Air pressure (atm)	1 atm
Volume of gas collected (L)	0.490 L

Cleanup and Disposal

1. Dispose of the empty can according to the instructions on its label.
2. Pour the water down the drain.
3. Discard any tape and the pipettes in the trash can.
4. Return all lab equipment to its proper place.

CHEMLAB 14

Analyze and Conclude

1. **Using Numbers** Fill in the remainder of the data table by calculating the mass of the gas that was released from the aerosol can, converting the atmospheric pressure from the units measured into atmospheres, and converting the air temperature into kelvins. Substitute your data from the table into the form of the ideal gas equation that solves for M. Calculate the molar mass of the gas in the can using the appropriate value for R.
   Sample calculation: Subtract the mass after release from the mass before release. 2.1 g
   Use °C + 273 = K to convert 25°C to 298 K. M = mRT/PV = 105 g/mol

2. **Using Numbers** Read the contents of the can and determine which of the gases from step 4 in the Pre-Lab is the most likely propellant.
   $C_2H_2F_4$ has a molar mass of 102 g/mol and is the most likely propellant.

3. **Error Analysis** Remember that you are collecting the gas after it has bubbled through water. What might happen to some of the gas as it goes through the water? What might be present in the gas in the beaker in addition to the gas from the can? Calculate the percent error using your calculated molar mass compared to the molar mass of the gas in the aerosol can.
   Some of the gas might dissolve in the water. Water vapor might be present.
   Sample calculation: (105 − 102)/102 × 100% = 2.94% error

4. **Interpreting Data** Were your data consistent with the ideal gas law? Evaluate the pressure and temperature at which your experiment was done, and the polarity of the gas. Would you expect the gas in your experiment to behave as an ideal gas or a real gas?
   No; the gas would behave as a real gas.

Real-World Chemistry

1. Explain why the label on an aerosol can warns against exposing the can to high heat.
   As temperature increases, pressure increases. If the pressure increases enough, the container might explode.

2. Use the ideal gas law to explain why the wind blows.
   Assume the volume of air and the temperature are constant. Using the ideal gas equation, PV = nRT, as pressure increases, the amount of gas also increases, as all other values are constant. Thus, when air pressure drops, air moves (wind blows) from an area of high pressure to an area of low pressure.

Copyright © Glencoe/McGraw-Hill, a division of the McGraw-Hill Companies, Inc.

miniLAB 15
Freezing Point Depression

Measuring The colligative property of freezing point depression can be observed in a simple laboratory investigation. You will measure the temperatures of two beakers and their contents.

Materials 400-mL beakers (2), crushed ice, rock salt (NaCl), water, stirring rods (2), graduated cylinder, thermometers (2), balance

Procedure

1. Fill two 400-mL beakers with crushed ice. Add 50 mL of cold tap water to each beaker.

2. Stir the contents of each beaker with a stirring rod until both beakers are at a constant temperature, approximately 1 minute.

3. Measure the temperature of each beaker using a thermometer and record the readings.

4. Add 75 g of rock salt to one of the beakers. Continue stirring both beakers. Some of the salt will dissolve.

5. When the temperature in each beaker is constant, record the readings.

6. To clean up, flush the contents of each beaker down the drain with excess water.

Expected Results: The salt will lower the freezing point of the water 4 to 6°C.

Analysis

1. Compare your readings taken for the ice water and the salt water. How do you explain the observed temperature change?
   The freezing point of the water was lowered 4–6°C by the addition of the salt. The ions interfere with the attractive forces between water molecules, thus preventing the water from freezing at its normal freezing temperature of 0°C.

2. Why was salt only added to one of the beakers?
   The beaker containing only ice serves as the control.

3. Salt is a strong electrolyte that produces two ions, Na^+ and Cl^-, when it dissociates in water. Why is this important to consider when calculating the colligative property of freezing point depression?
   The number of particles in the solution affects the colligative properties of a solution. Because one mole of sodium chloride produces two moles of ions in solution, it has a greater effect on the freezing point and boiling point than a solute that produces only one mole of particles in solution.

4. Predict if it would be better to use coarse rock salt or fine table salt when making homemade ice cream. Explain.
   Fine table salt is a better choice because it dissolves more quickly in the cold water than coarse rock salt does, thus, producing the greatest freezing point depression as quickly as possible.

CHEMLAB 15
Beer's Law

Finding the concentration of an unknown solution is an important procedure in laboratory work. One method commonly used to determine solution concentration is to measure how much of a single wavelength of light is absorbed by the solution and compare it to known values of concentration and wavelength. Light absorbance is directly related to the concentration of a solution. This relationship is called Beer's law.

Problem

How is light absorbance used to find the concentration of a blue dye solution?

Objectives

- **Prepare** solutions of known concentration from a blue dye stock solution.
- **Measure** the absorbance of known and unknown aqueous solutions.
- **Infer** the relationship between light absorbance and concentration of a solution.

Materials

CBL system
graphing calculator
Vernier colorimeter
DIN adapter and cable
TI GRAPH LINK (optional)
cuvette
cotton swabs
tissues for wiping cuvette

blue dye stock solution
unknown solution
distilled water
50-mL graduated cylinder
100-mL beaker (2)
small test tube (5)
test-tube rack
pipette (2)
pipette bulb
stirring rod

Safety Precautions

- Always wear safety goggles and a lab apron.
- The food-coloring solution can stain clothes.

Pre-Lab

1. Read the entire CHEMLAB procedure.

2. What is the total volume of solution in each test tube? Calculate the percent by volume of the solutions in test tubes 1 through 5. Use the data table on the next page.
   Each test tube contains 10mL. % by volume: 1, 20%; 2, 40%; 3, 60%; 4, 80%; 5, 100%

3. Review with your teacher how a colorimeter works. How are absorbance (A) and transmittance (%T) related?
   $A = \log(100/\%T)$

4. What is occurring during step 3 of the procedure? Why is a cuvette of water used?
   The colorimeter is being calibrated for red light. The cuvette of water is used as a measure of 100%T because it contains no blue dye solution.

CHEMLAB 15

Procedure

1. Transfer 30 mL of blue dye stock solution into a beaker. Transfer 30 mL of distilled water into another beaker.

2. Label five clean, dry test tubes 1 through 5.

3. Pipette 2 mL of blue dye stock solution from the beaker into test tube 1, 4 mL into test tube 2, 6 mL into test tube 3, and 8 mL into test tube 4. **CAUTION:** *Always pipette using a pipette bulb.*

4. With another pipette, transfer 8 mL of distilled water from the beaker into test tube 1, 6 mL into tube 2, 4 mL into tube 3, and 2 mL into tube 4.

5. Mix the solution in test tube 1 with a stirring rod. Rinse and dry the stirring rod. Repeat this procedure with each test tube.

6. Pipette 10 mL of blue dye stock into test tube 5.

7. Load the ChemBio program into the calculator. Connect the CBL to the colorimeter using a DIN adapter. Connect the CBL to the calculator using a link cable. Begin the ChemBio program on the calculator. Select "1" probe. Select 4: COLORIMETER. Enter Channel "1."

8. Fill a cuvette about three-fourths full with distilled water and dry its outside with a tissue. To calibrate the colorimeter, place the cuvette in the colorimeter and close the lid. Turn the wavelength knob to 0%T. Press TRIGGER on the CBL and enter 0 into the calculator. Turn the wavelength knob to Red (635 nm). Press TRIGGER on the CBL and enter 100 into the calculator. Leave the colorimeter set on Red for the rest of the lab. Remove the cuvette from the colorimeter. Empty the distilled water from the cuvette. Dry the inside of the cuvette with a clean cotton swab.

9. Select COLLECT DATA from the MAIN MENU. Select TRIGGER/PROMPT from the DATA COLLECTION menu. Fill the cuvette about three-fourths full with the solution from test tube 1. Dry the outside of the cuvette with a tissue and place the cuvette in the colorimeter. Close the lid. After 10 to 15 seconds, press TRIGGER and enter the concentration in percent from your data table into the calculator.

Sample Data

Known and Unknown Solutions Data

Test tube	Concentration (%)	%T	A
1	20	88.888	0.05116
2	40	72.934	0.13707
3	60	61.253	0.21287
4	80	53.846	0.26885
5	100	44.729	0.34941
Unknown	*		

* Depends on solution prepared by instructor.

Remove the cuvette and pour out the solution. Rinse the inside of the cuvette with distilled water and dry it with a clean cotton swab. Repeat this step for test tubes 2 through 5.

10. Select STOP AND GRAPH from the DATA COLLECTION menu when you have finished with data collection. Draw the graph, or use the TI Graph-Link to make a copy of the graph from the calculator screen. You also will want to copy the data from the STAT list into your data table (or you can print it from a screen print using Graph-Link).

11. Clean the cuvette with a cotton swab and fill it about three-fourths full with the unknown dye solution. Place the cuvette in the colorimeter and close the lid. From the MAIN MENU, select COLLECT DATA (do not select SET UP PROBES as this will erase your data lists). Select MONITOR INPUT from the DATA COLLECTION MENU. Press ENTER to monitor the absorbance value of the colorimeter. After about 10–15 seconds, record the absorbance value and record it in your data table.

Cleanup and Disposal

1. All of the blue dye solutions can be rinsed down the drain.

2. Turn off the colorimeter. Clean and dry the cuvette. Return all equipment to its proper place.

CHEMLAB 15

Analyze and Conclude

1. **Analyzing Data** Evaluate how close your graph is to the direct relationship exhibited by Beer's law by doing a linear-regression line. Select FIT CURVE from the MAIN MENU (do not select SET UP PROBES as this will erase your data lists). Select LINEAR L1,L2. The calculator will give you an equation in the form of $y = ax + b$. A small value of b means the graph passes close to the origin. The closer the correlation coefficient r reported by the program is to 1.00, the better the fit of the graph.

    See sample graph in Solutions Manual. The sample data results in $b = -0.0146$ and $r = 0.998$. These values show a good correlation to Beer's law.

2. **Drawing Conclusions** Use the graph of your absorbance and concentration data to determine the concentration of your unknown solution.

    Answers will vary. A solution with an absorbance of 0.127 will have a concentration of 39%.

3. **Form a Hypothesis** Would you obtain the same data if red dye was used? Explain.

    The color of the solution is due to reflected light. The blue dye solution reflects blue light and absorbs red. A red dye solution would absorb blue and reflect red. If the procedure was repeated with red dye solution, no red light would be absorbed. Absorbance readings would not be obtained.

4. **Error Analysis** Analyze your b and r values. How closely do your results match Beer's law? Reexamine the procedure and suggest reasons why the correlation coefficient from your data does not equal 1.00.

    Accurate results would not be obtained if the solutions were not prepared carefully, the cuvette was not cleaned and dried adequately between solutions, more than one cuvette was used, the cuvette was not consistently aligned in the colorimeter, or data were not entered correctly.

Real-World Chemistry

1. Explain how Beer's law can be applied in food, drug, and medical testing.

    This method can be used to find concentrations of colored solutions such as fruit juices or colored drug preparations.

2. The reaction of alcohol with orange dichromate ions to produce blue-green chromium(III) ions is used in the Breathalyzer test, a test that measures the presence of alcohol in a person's breath. How could a colorimeter be used in this analysis?

    A color scale relating the blue-green color and alcohol concentration could be used.

Name _____ Date _____ Class _____

miniLAB 16
Enthalpy of Fusion for Ice

Applying Concepts When ice is added to water at room temperature, the water provides the energy for two processes. The first process is the melting of the ice. The energy required to melt ice is the enthalpy of fusion (ΔH_{fus}). The second process is raising the temperature of the melted ice from its initial temperature of 0.0°C to the final temperature of the liquid water. In this experiment, you will collect data to calculate the enthalpy of fusion for ice.

Materials foam cup, thermometer, stirring rod, ice, water, balance

Procedure

1. Measure the mass of an empty foam cup and record it in your data table.
2. Fill the foam cup about one-third full of water. Measure and record the mass.
3. Place the thermometer in the cup. Read and record the initial temperature of the water.
4. Quickly place a small quantity of ice in the foam cup. Gently stir the water with a stirring rod until the ice melts. Record the lowest temperature reached as the final temperature.
5. Measure the mass of the cup and water.

Analysis

1. The heat lost by the liquid water equals the heat needed to melt the ice plus the heat needed to increase the temperature of the melted ice from 0.0°C to the final temperature. Calculate the heat lost by the water.

   q_{water} = **4.184 J/(g·°C) × 153.70 g × 8.0°C = 5100 J**

2. Calculate the heat gained by the melted ice as its temperature rose from 0.0°C to the final temperature.

   $q_{melted\ ice}$ = **4.184 J/(g·°C) × 14.76 g × 13.0°C = 803 J**

3. The difference between the heat lost by the water and the heat gained by the melted ice equals the heat of fusion. Calculate the heat of fusion in joules per gram of ice.

   (5100 J − 800 J)/14.76 g = 290 J/g

4. Calculate ΔH_{fus} in kJ/mol.

   290 J/g × 1 kJ/1000 J × 18.02 g/mol = 5.2 kJ/mol

5. Calculate the percent error of your experimental ΔH_{fus}. Compare your value to the actual value 6.01 kJ/mol.

   ((6.01 − 5.2)/6.01) × 100 = 13% error

Expected Results: mass of cup = 3.97 g; mass of water + cup = 157.67 g; mass of liquid water = 153.70 g; mass of cup + water + melted ice = 172.43 g; mass of melted ice = 14.76 g; ΔT (liquid water) = 21.0°C − 13.0°C = 8.0°C; ΔT (melted ice) = 13.0°C − 0.0°C = 13.0°C

Name _____ Date _____ Class _____

CHEMLAB 16
Calorimetry

In this laboratory investigation, you will use the methods of calorimetry to approximate the amount of energy contained in a potato chip. The burning of a potato chip releases heat stored in the substances contained in the chip. The heat will be absorbed by a mass of water.

Problem
How many Calories of energy does the potato chip contain? How can the experiment be improved to provide a more accurate answer?

Objectives
• **Identify** the reactants and products in the reaction.
• **Measure** mass and temperature in order to calculate the amount of heat released in the reaction.
• **Propose** changes in the procedure and design of the equipment to decrease the percent error.

Materials
large potato chip
250-mL beaker
100-mL graduated cylinder
evaporating dish
thermometer
ring stand with ring
wire gauze
matches
stirring rod
balance

Safety Precautions
• Always wear safety goggles and a lab apron.
• Tie back long hair.
• Hot objects may not appear to be hot.
• Do not heat broken, chipped, or cracked glassware.
• Do not eat any items used in the lab.

Pre-Lab
1. Read the entire CHEMLAB.
2. Prepare all written materials that you will take into the laboratory. Be sure to include safety precautions and procedure notes. Use the data table on the next page.
3. Form a hypothesis about how the quantity of heat produced by the combustion reaction will compare with the quantity of heat absorbed by the water. **The quantity of heat produced by the reaction will exceed the quantity of heat absorbed by the water.**
4. What formula will you use to calculate the quantity of heat absorbed by the water? **q = c × m × ΔT**
5. Assuming that the potato chip contains compounds made up of carbon and hydrogen, what gases will be produced in the combustion reaction? **carbon dioxide and water vapor**

CHEMLAB 16

Procedure

1. Measure the mass of a potato chip and record it in the data table.

2. Place the potato chip in an evaporating dish on the metal base of the ring stand. Position the ring and wire gauze so that they will be 10 cm above the top of the potato chip.

3. Measure the mass of an empty 250-mL beaker and record it in the data table.

4. Using the graduated cylinder, measure 50 mL of water and pour it into the beaker. Measure the mass of the beaker and water and record it in the data table.

5. Place the beaker on the wire gauze on the ring stand.

6. Measure and record the initial temperature of the water.

7. Use a match to ignite the bottom of the potato chip.

8. With a stirring rod, stir the water in the beaker while the chip burns. Measure the highest temperature of the water and record it in the data table.

Analyze and Conclude

1. **Classifying** Is the reaction exothermic or endothermic? Explain how you know.
The reaction is exothermic because heat and light were visible and the temperature of the water increased.

2. **Observing and Inferring** Describe the reactant and products of the chemical reaction. Was the reactant (potato chip) completely consumed? What evidence supports your answer?
The potato chip burns in oxygen from the air to produce carbon dioxide gas, water vapor, and unburned carbon. The chip was not completely consumed as indicated by the presence of soot and ash.

3. **Using Numbers** Calculate the mass of water in the beaker and the temperature change of the water. Use $q = c \times m \times \Delta T$ to calculate how much heat in joules was transferred to the water in the beaker by the burning of one chip.
50.26 g water, 15.3 °C; $q = c \times m \times \Delta T$;
$q = 4.184 \ J/(g \cdot °C) \times 50.26 \ g \times 15.3°C = 3220 \ J/chip$

Sample Data

Observations of the Burning of a Potato Chip

Mass of beaker and 50 mL of water	148.26 g
Mass of empty beaker	98.00 g
Mass of water in beaker	50.26 g
Mass of potato chip	1.63 g
Highest temperature of water	37.4°C
Initial temperature of water	22.1°C
Change in temperature	15.3°C

Cleanup and Disposal

1. Clean all lab equipment and return it to its proper place.

2. Wash your hands thoroughly after all lab work and cleanup is complete.

CHEMLAB 16

4. **Using Numbers** Convert the quantity of heat in joules/chip to Calories/chip.
3220 J/chip × 1 cal/4.184 J × 1 Calorie/1000 cal = 0.770 Calories

5. **Using Numbers** From the information on the chip's container, determine the mass in grams of one serving. Using your data, calculate the number of Calories that would be released by the combustion of one serving of chips.
28 g per serving: 0.770 Calories/1.63 g × 28 g/1 serving = 13.2 Calories

6. **Error Analysis** Use the chip's container to determine how many Calories are contained in one serving. Compare your calculated Calories per serving with the value on the chip's container. Calculate the percent error.
75 Calories per serving, but answers will vary according to the snack used
(75 Calories − 13.2 Calories)/75 Calories × 100 = 82% error.

7. **Observing and Inferring** Was all of the heat that was released collected by the water in the beaker? How can the experimental equipment be improved to decrease the percent error?
No; The air, glass beaker, and wire gauze absorbed heat from the flame, contributing to the high percent error. An insulated container would improve the experimental design.

Real-World Chemistry

1. From the ingredients identified on the potato chip container, list the actual substances that burned to produce energy. Are there any ingredients that did not produce energy? Explain.
A potato chip is mostly the carbohydrate contained in potatoes and fats. These are the substances that burned. If the potato chip was salted, the salt would not burn to produce energy.

2. You have discovered that potato chips provide a significant number of Calories per serving. Would it be advisable to make potato chips a substantial part of your diet? Explain.
The contents of potato chips are too limited to provide a healthy diet if made a substantial part of a diet.

Copyright © Glencoe/McGraw-Hill, a division of the McGraw-Hill Companies, Inc.

miniLAB 17

Examining Reaction Rate and Temperature

Recognizing Cause and Effect Several factors affect the rate of a chemical reaction. This lab allows you to examine the effect of temperature on a common chemical reaction.

Materials small beaker, thermometer, hot plate, 250-mL beaker, balance, water, effervescent (bicarbonate) tablet, stopwatch or clock with second hand

Procedure

1. Take a single effervescent tablet and break it into four roughly equal pieces.
2. Measure the mass of one piece of the tablet. Measure 50 mL of room-temperature water (approximately 20°C) into a small cup or beaker. Measure the temperature of the water.
3. With a stopwatch ready, add the piece of tablet to the water. Record the amount of time elapsed between when the tablet hits the water and when you see that all of the piece of tablet has dissolved in the water.
4. Repeat steps 2 and 3 twice more, except use water temperatures of about 50°C and 65°C. Be sure to raise the temperature gradually and maintain the desired temperature (equilibrate) throughout the run.

Analysis

1. Calculate the reaction rate by finding the mass/time for each run. Use the data table below.
2. Graph the reaction rate (mass/time) versus temperature for the runs in the space below.
3. What is the relationship between reaction rate and temperature for this reaction?

As temperature increases, the reaction rate increases.

4. Using your graphed data, predict the reaction rate for the reaction carried out at 40°C. Heat and equilibrate the water to 40°C and use the last piece of tablet to test your prediction.

Answers will vary; however, prediction is about 0.047 g/s.

5. How did your prediction for the reaction rate at 40°C compare to the actual reaction rate?

Answers will vary. The value may not be as predicted due to experimental errors.

Sample Data

Data Table		
Mass of Tablet (g)	Reaction time (s)	Reaction rate (g/s)	Temperature (°C)
0.92	27.56	0.033	23.6
0.79	13.22	0.060	53.4
0.89	13.77	0.065	64.0
0.54	11.38	0.047	40.0

(Analysis 4 trial)

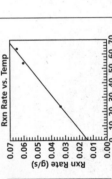

Rxn Rate vs. Temp

Rxn Rate (g/s) — axis values: 0.07, 0.06, 0.05, 0.04, 0.03, 0.02, 0.01, 0.00
Temp (Celsius) — axis values: 10 20 30 40 50 60 70

CHEMLAB 17

Concentration and Reaction Rate

The collision theory describes how the change in concentration of one reactant affects the rate of chemical reactions. In this laboratory experiment, you will observe how concentration affects the reaction rate.

Problem

How does the concentration of a reactant affect the reaction rate?

Objectives

- **Sequence** the acid concentrations from the most to the least concentrated.
- **Observe** which concentration results in the fastest reaction rate.

Materials

10-mL graduated pipette
safety pipette filler
6M hydrochloric acid
distilled water
25 mm × 150 mm test tubes (4)
test-tube rack
magnesium ribbon
emery cloth or fine sandpaper
scissors
plastic ruler
tongs
watch with second hand
stirring rod

Safety Precautions

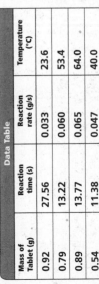

- Always wear safety goggles and a lab apron.
- Never pipette any chemical by mouth.
- Do not have any open flames in the room.

Pre-Lab

1. Read the entire CHEMLAB. Prepare all written materials that you will take into the laboratory. Be sure to include safety precautions and procedure notes. Use the data table on the next page.
2. Use emery paper or sandpaper to polish the magnesium ribbon until it is shiny. Use scissors to cut the magnesium into four 1-cm pieces.
3. Place the four test tubes in the test-tube rack. Label the test tubes #1 (6.0M HCl), #2 (3M HCl), #3 (1.5M HCl), and #4 (0.75M HCl).
4. Form a hypothesis about how the chemical reaction rate is related to reactant concentration.

Students' hypotheses should reflect that the reaction rate is faster with higher concentration; slower with lower concentration.

5. What reactant quantity is held constant? What are the independent and dependent variables?

The amount of Mg is the constant.

[HCl] is the independent variable.

Time is the dependent variable.

6. What gas is produced in the reaction between magnesium and hydrochloric acid? Write the balanced formula equation for the reaction.

hydrogen gas; $Mg(s) + 2HCl(aq) \rightarrow MgCl_2(s) + H_2(g)$

7. Why is it important to clean the magnesium ribbon? If one of the four pieces is not thoroughly polished, how will the rate of the reaction involving that piece be affected?
Cleaning removes any deposits on the metal and exposes the entire magnesium surface for reaction. If a piece of magnesium is not clean, the reaction rate will be slower.

Procedure

1. Use a safety pipette filler to draw 10 mL of 6.0M hydrochloric acid (HCl) into a 10-mL graduated pipette.
2. Dispense the 10 mL of 6.0M HCl into test tube #1.
3. Draw 5.0 mL of the 6.0M HCl from test tube #1 with the empty pipette. Dispense this acid into test tube #2 and use the pipette to add an additional 5.0 mL of distilled water to the acid. Use the stirring rod to mix thoroughly. This solution is 3.0M HCl.
4. Draw 5.0 mL of the 3.0M HCl from test tube #2 with the empty pipette. Dispense this acid into test tube #3 and use the pipette to add an additional 5.0 mL of distilled water to the acid. Use the stirring rod to mix thoroughly. This solution is 1.5M HCl.
5. Draw 5.0 mL of the 1.5M HCl from test tube #3 with the empty pipette. Dispense this acid into test tube #4 and use the pipette to add an additional 5.0 mL of distilled water to the acid. Use the stirring rod to mix thoroughly. This solution is 0.75M HCl.
6. Draw 5.0 mL of the 0.75M HCl from test tube #4 with the empty pipette. Neutralize and discard it in the sink.
7. Using the tongs, place a 1-cm length of magnesium ribbon into test tube #1. Record the time in seconds that it takes for the bubbling to stop.
8. Repeat step 7 using the remaining three test tubes of HCl and the three remaining pieces of magnesium ribbon. Record in the data table the time (in seconds) it takes for the bubbling to stop.

Reaction Time Data

Test tube	[HCl] (M)	Time (s)
1	6.0	5
2	3.0	25
3	1.5	40
4	0.75	110

Cleanup and Disposal

1. Place acid solutions in an acid discard container. Your teacher will neutralize the acid for proper disposal.
2. Wash thoroughly all test tubes and lab equipment.
3. Discard other materials as directed by your teacher.
4. Return all lab equipment to its proper place.

Analyze and Conclude

1. Analyzing In step 6, why is 5.0 mL HCl discarded? **The volume in each test tube must be the same, 5.0 mL.**
2. Making and Using Graphs Plot the concentration of the acid on the x-axis and time it takes for the bubbling to stop on the y-axis. Draw a smooth curve through the data points.

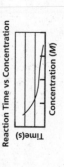

Reaction Time vs Concentration

Time(s) — Concentration (M)

---

3. Interpreting Graphs Is the curve in question 2 linear or nonlinear? What does the slope tell you? **nonlinear; Reaction time and concentration are inversely related.**
4. Drawing a Conclusion Based on your graph, what do you conclude about the relationship between the acid concentration and the reaction rate? **Because the acid concentration is inversely related to the reaction time, reaction time decreases as concentration increases.**
5. Hypothesizing Write a hypothesis using the collision theory, reaction rate, and reactant concentration to explain your results.
As the concentration of the HCl reactant increases in the test tube, the probability of an effective collision with the Mg metal increases. These collisions displace H_2 gas from the acid, increasing the rate of the reaction as is evidenced by increased bubbling.
6. Designing an Experiment Write a brief statement of how you would set up an experiment to test your hypothesis.
Student answers will vary. An example is an experiment to perform a combustion reaction with increasing concentrations of oxygen to verify the increased rate of combustion.
7. Error Analysis Compare your experimental results with those of several other students in the laboratory. Explain the differences.
Errors may arise from differences in measuring and/or inaccurate pipetting in the series from test tubes 1–4. Students may also record variances in the time they first see bubbles.

Real-World Chemistry

1. Describe a situation that may occur in your daily life that exemplifies the effect of concentration on the rate of a reaction.
Answers will vary. For example, students might relate the concentration of chlorine in a pool to control algae growth, or they might describe how the concentration of powdered drink mix affects the solution.
2. Some hair-care products, such as hot-oil treatments, must be heated before application. Explain in terms of factors affecting reaction rates why heat is required.
Heat increases the kinetic activity of the molecules, which in turn increases the number of high-energy collisions that will overcome the activation energy barrier and form the desired products (and effects). If the reactants remained unheated, the desired product would not form.

Name _____ Date _____ Class _____

miniLAB 18
Shifts in Equilibrium

Observing and Inferring Le Châtelier's principle states that if a stress is placed on a reaction at equilibrium, the system will shift in a way that will relieve the stress. In this experiment, you will witness an equilibrium shift in a colorful way.

Materials test tubes (2); 10-mL graduated cylinder; 250-mL beaker; concentrated hydrochloric acid; 0.1M CoCl₂ solution; ice bath; table salt; hot plate

Procedures

1. Place about 2 mL of $0.1M$ $CoCl_2$ solution in a test tube. Record the color of the solution. **pink**

2. Add about 3 mL of concentrated HCl to the test tube. Record the color of the solution. **CAUTION:** *HCl can burn skin and clothing.* **blue**

3. Add enough water to the test tube to make a color change occur. Record the color. **pink**

4. Add about 2 mL of $0.1M$ $CoCl_2$ to another test tube. Add concentrated HCl dropwise until the solution turns purple. If the solution becomes blue, add water until it turns purple.

5. Place the test tube in an ice bath that has had some salt sprinkled into the ice water. Record the color of the solution in the test tube. **pink**

6. Place the test tube in a hot water bath that is at least 70°C. Record the color of the solution. **blue**

Analysis

1. The equation for the reversible reaction in this experiment is

$$Co(H_2O)_6^{2+} + 4Cl^- \rightleftharpoons CoCl_4^{2-} + 6H_2O$$
  pink   blue

Use the equation to explain your observations of color in steps 1–3.
The addition of excess chloride ions from the HCl pushes the equilibrium toward the blue ion. Addition of water pushes it back toward the pink ion.

2. Explain how the equilibrium shifts when energy is added or removed.
Because the blue ion formed when heat was added, the formation of the blue ion is endothermic. The formation of the pink ion is exothermic.

Expected Results: Addition of HCl to the pink solution produces a blue solution. When water is added to the blue solution, it turns pink. The purple solution will turn pink in the ice bath, but turns blue in the hot-water bath.

Name _____ Date _____ Class _____

CHEMLAB 18

Comparing Two Solubility Product Constants

Le Châtelier's principle is a powerful tool for explaining how a reaction at equilibrium shifts when a stress is placed on the system. In this experiment, you can use Le Châtelier's principle to evaluate the relative solubilities of two precipitates. By observing the formation of two precipitates in the same system, you can infer the relationship between the solubilities of the two ionic compounds and the numerical values of their solubility product constants (K_{sp}). You will be able to verify your own experimental results by calculating the molar solubilities of the two compounds using the K_{sp} for each compound.

Problem

How can a saturated solution of one ionic compound react with another ionic compound to form another precipitate? What is the relationship between solubility and the K_{sp} value of a saturated solution?

Objectives

• **Observe** evidence that a precipitate is in equilibrium with its ions in solution.
• **Infer** the relative solubilities of two sparingly soluble ionic compounds.
• **Compare** the values of the K_{sp} for two different compounds and relate them to your observations.
• **Explain** your observations of the two precipitates by using Le Châtelier's principle.
• **Calculate** the molar solubilities of the two ionic compounds from their K_{sp} values.

Safety Precautions

• Always wear safety goggles, gloves, and a lab apron.
• Silver nitrate is highly toxic and will stain skin and clothing.

Pre-Lab

1. Read the entire CHEMLAB.

2. Prepare all written materials that you will take into the laboratory. Be sure to include safety precautions and procedure notes. Use the data table on the next page.

3. State Le Châtelier's principle.
Le Châtelier's principle states that if stress is applied to a system at equilibrium, the system shifts in the direction that relieves the stress.

4. Identify the control and the independent variable in the experiment.
The control is the solution in well A1.
The independent variable is the solution in well A2.

5. When a solid dissolves to form two ions and the solid's K_{sp} is known, what is the mathematical formula you can use to calculate the molar solubility?
molar solubility s $= \sqrt{K_{sp}}$

Expected Results: When the first two solutions are mixed, a white precipitate of $PbSO_4$ forms. The color of the precipitate changes from white to black when the ammonium sulfide solution is added, producing the PbS precipitate.

Materials

$AgNO_3$ solution
NaCl solution
Na_2S solution
24-well microplate
thin-stem pipettes (3)
wash bottle

CHEMLAB 18

Procedure

1. Place 10 drops of $AgNO_3$ solution in well A1 of a 24-well microplate. Place 10 drops of the same solution in well A2.

2. Add 10 drops of NaCl solution to well A1 and 10 drops to well A2.

3. Allow the precipitate to form in each well. Record your observations.

4. To well A2, add 10 drops of Na_2S solution.

5. Allow the precipitate to form. Record your observations of the precipitate.

6. Compare the contents of wells A1 and A2 and record your observations in the data table.

Cleanup and Disposal

1. Use a wash bottle to transfer the contents of the well plate into a large waste beaker.

2. Wash your hands thoroughly after all lab work and cleanup are complete.

Precipitate Formation

	Observations
Step 3	White precipitate in both wells.
Step 5	A black precipitate forms.
Step 6	White precipitate disappears.

Analyze and Conclude

1. **Analyzing Information** Write the complete equation for the double-replacement reaction that occurred when NaCl and $AgNO_3$ were mixed in wells A1 and A2 in step 2. Write the net ionic equation.

$$AgNO_3(aq) + NaCl(aq) \rightarrow AgCl(s) + NaNO_3(aq)$$

$$AgCl(s) \rightleftharpoons Ag^+(aq) + Cl^-(aq)$$

2. **Analyzing Information** Write the solubility product constant expression for the equilibrium established in wells A1 and A2 in step 2. K_{sp} (AgCl) = 1.8×10^{-10}.

$$K_{sp} = [Ag^+][Cl^-] = 1.8 \times 10^{-10}$$

3. **Analyzing Information** Write the equation for the equilibrium that was established in well A2 when you added Na_2S. K_{sp} (Ag_2S) = 8×10^{-48}

$$2AgCl(s) + Na_2S(aq) \rightarrow Ag_2S(s) + 2NaCl; Ag_2S(s) \rightleftharpoons 2Ag^+(aq) + S^{2-}(aq)$$

4. **Inferring** Identify the two precipitates by color. __AgCl: white; Ag₂S: black__

5. **Comparing and Contrasting** Compare the K_{sp} values for the two precipitates. Infer which of the two ionic compounds is more soluble.

K_{sp} (AgCl) = 1.8×10^{-10}; K_{sp} (Ag_2S) = 8×10^{-48}; AgCl is more soluble.

6. **Recognizing Cause and Effect** Use Le Châtelier's principle to explain how the addition of $(NH_4)_2S$ in procedure step 4 affected the equilibrium established in well A2. Silver ions are in equilibrium with solid white AgCl. On the addition of Na_2S, S^{2-} ions combine with Ag^+ ions to form solid, black Ag_2S. According to Le Châtelier's principle, the removal of the Ag^+ ions shifts the AgCl equilibrium to the right, thus dissolving AgCl as Ag_2 forms.

CHEMLAB 18

7. **Using Numbers** Calculate the molar solubilities of the two precipitates using the K_{sp} values. Which of the precipitates is more soluble? Solubility AgCl = $1.3 \times 10^{-5}M$. Solubility Ag_2S = $1 \times 10^{-16}M$;

AgCl is more soluble.

8. **Thinking Critically** What evidence from this experiment supports your answer to question 7? Explain.

See the Solutions Manual.

9. **Error Analysis** Did you observe the well plate from the side as well as from the top? What did you notice?

See the Solutions Manual.

10. **Developing General Rules** The solubility of an ionic compound depends upon the nature of the cations and anions that make up the compound. The reactants you used in this CHEMLAB are all soluble ionic compounds, whereas the precipitates are insoluble. How does soluble Na_2S differ from insoluble Ag_2S? How does soluble NaCl differ from insoluble AgCl? Use this information and K_{sp} data from **Table 18-3** and the *Handbook of Chemistry and Physics* to develop general rules for solubility. What group of metal ions is not found in sparingly soluble compounds? What polyatomic ions, positive and negative, form only soluble ionic compounds? How does K_{sp} relate to a compound's relative solubility?

See the Solutions Manual.

Real-World Chemistry

1. Research how industries use precipitation to remove hazardous chemicals from waste-water before returning it to the water cycle.

Toxic heavy metals in wastewater are often precipitated in large holding ponds. The water is then released, and the sludge is removed to a hazardous waste facility.

2. *Hard water* is the name given to water supplies that contain significant concentrations of Mg^{2+} and Ca^{2+} ions. Check on the solubility of ionic compounds formed with these ions and predict what problems they may cause.

Ca and Mg ions form many insoluble compounds that deposit in water pipes and precipitate as soap scum.

3. Explain what would happen if you lost the stopper for a bottle of a saturated solution of lead sulfate ($PbSO_4$) and the bottle stood open to the air for a week. Would your answer be different if it was an unsaturated solution? Explain.

A precipitate would form as the water evaporated. For an unsaturated solution, the process would take longer.

miniLAB 19
Acid Strength

Observing and Inferring The electrical conductivities of solutions of weak acids, such as acetic acid, are related to the degree of ionization of the acid.

Materials glacial acetic acid; distilled water; 10-mL graduated cylinder; dropping pipette; 50-mL beaker; 24-well microplate; conductivity tester with battery; stirring rod

Procedure

1. Use a 10-mL graduated cylinder to measure 3 mL of glacial acetic acid. Use a dropping pipette to transfer the 3 mL of glacial acetic acid into well A1 of a 24-well microplate.

2. Lower the electrodes of a conductivity tester into the glacial acetic acid in well A1. Record your results.

3. Rinse the graduated cylinder with water. Prepare a 6.0M solution of acetic acid by adding 3.4 mL of glacial acetic acid to 6.6 mL of distilled water in the 10-mL graduated cylinder.

4. Empty the 10 mL of diluted acid into a 50-mL beaker. After mixing, transfer 3 mL of the 6.0M acetic acid into well A2. Save the remaining 6.0M acetic acid for procedure step 5. Test and record the conductivity of the solution.

5. Prepare a 1.0M acetic acid solution by adding 1.7 mL of 6.0M acetic acid to 8.3 mL of distilled water in the 10-mL graduated cylinder. Empty the 10 mL of diluted acid into the rinsed 50-mL beaker. After mixing, transfer 3 mL of the 1.0M acetic acid into well A3. Save the remaining 1.0M acetic acid for procedure step 6. Test and record the conductivity of solution.

6. Prepare a 0.1M acetic acid solution by adding 1.0 mL of 1.0M acetic acid to 9.0 mL of distilled acid into the rinsed 10-mL graduated cylinder. Empty the 10 mL of diluted acid into the rinsed 50-mL beaker. After mixing, transfer 3 mL of the 0.1M acetic acid into well A4. Test and record the conductivity of the solution.

Expected Results: The glacial acetic acid does not conduct electricity, so neither the red nor the green LED glows. For all of the dilutions, the red LED on the tester glows brightly. For the 6.0M acetic acid solution, the green LED is dim; for 1.0M acid, the green LED is bright; for 0.1M acid, the green LED is dimmer than for the 6.0M.

Analysis

1. Write the equation for the ionization of acetic acid in water and the equilibrium constant expression. ($K_{eq} = 1.8 \times 10^{-5}$) What does the size of K_{eq} indicate about the degree of ionization of acetic acid?
See the Solutions Manual.

2. Do the following approximate percents ionization fit your laboratory results: glacial acetic acid, 0.1%; 6.0M acetic acid, 0.2%; 1.0M acetic acid, 0.4%; 0.1M acetic acid, 1.3%? Explain.
See the Solutions Manual.

3. State a hypothesis that will explain your observations and incorporate your answer to Question 2.
See the Solutions Manual.

4. Based on your hypothesis, what can you conclude about the need to use large amounts of water for rinsing when acid spills on living tissue?
See the Solutions Manual.

CHEMLAB 19

Standardizing a Base Solution by Titration

The procedure called titration can be used to standardize a solution of a base, which means determine its molar concentration. To standardize a base, a solution of the base with unknown molarity is gradually added to a solution containing a known mass of an acid. The procedure enables you to determine when the number of moles of added OH^- ions from the base equals the number of moles of H^+ ion from the acid.

Problem

How can you determine the molar concentration of a base solution? How do you know when the neutralization reaction has reached the equivalence point?

Objectives

- **Recognize** the color change of the indicator that shows that the equivalence point has been reached.
- **Measure** the mass of the acid and the volume of the base solution used.
- **Calculate** the molar concentration of the base solution.

Materials

50-mL burette
burette clamp
ring stand
sodium hydroxide pellets (NaOH)
potassium hydrogen phthalate ($KHC_8H_4O_4$)
distilled water
weighing bottle
spatula

250-mL Erlenmeyer flask
500-mL Florence flask and rubber stopper
250-mL beaker
centigram balance
wash bottle
phenolphthalein solution
dropper

Safety Precautions

- **Always wear safety goggles and a lab apron.**

Pre-Lab

1. What is the equivalence point of a titration? **the point in a titration when the number of moles of H^+ ions from the acid equals the number of moles of OH^- ions from CHEMLAB.**

2. Read the entire CHEMLAB.

3. What is the independent variable? The dependent variable? Constant? **independent variable, the mass of acid; dependent variable, the volume of base; constants, the drops of indicator and amounts of water**

4. When the solid acid dissolves to form ions, how many moles of H^+ ions are produced for every mole of acid used? **one mole of H^+ ions for each mole of acid used**

5. What is the formula used to calculate molarity? **molarity = moles of solute per liter of solution**

6. Prepare a data table that will accommodate multiple titration trials.

7. List safety precautions that must be taken. **Wear goggles, apron, and gloves. Handle glassware carefully. Do not allow chemicals to contact skin.**

CHEMLAB 19

Procedure

1. Place approximately 4 g NaOH in a 500-mL Florence flask. Add enough water to dissolve the pellets and bring the volume of the NaOH solution to about 400 mL. **CAUTION:** *The solution will get hot.* Keep the stopper in the flask.

2. Use the weighing bottle to mass by difference about 0.40 g of potassium hydrogen phthalate (molar mass = 204.32 g/mol) into a 250-mL Erlenmeyer flask. Record this data.

3. Using a wash bottle, rinse down the insides of the flask and add enough water to make about 50 mL of solution. Add 2 drops of phenolphthalein indicator solution.

4. Set up the burette as shown. Rinse the burette with about 10 mL of your base solution. Discard the rinse solution in a discard beaker.

5. Fill the burette with NaOH solution. To remove any air trapped in the tip, allow a small amount of the base to flow from the tip of the burette into the discard beaker. Read the burette to the nearest 0.02 mL and record this initial reading. The meniscus of the solution in the burette should be at eye level when you make a reading.

6. Place a piece of white paper under the burette. Allow the NaOH solution to flow slowly from the burette into the flask containing the acid. Control the flow of the base solution with your left hand, and gently swirl the flask with your right hand.

7. The NaOH solution may be added in a rapid stream of drops until the pink color begins to last longer as the flask is swirled. At this stage, begin adding the base drop by drop.

8. The equivalence point is reached when one additional drop of base turns the acid in the flask pink. The pink color should persist as the flask is swirled. Record the final volume in the burette.

9. Calculate the molarity of your base using steps 2–5 on the next page.

10. Refill your burette with base. Rinse your Erlenmeyer flask with water. Repeat the titration with additional samples of acid until you get three trials that show close agreement between the calculated values of the molarity.

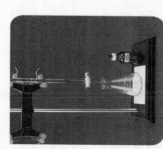

Cleanup and Disposal

1. The neutralized solutions can be washed down the sink using plenty of water.

Sample Data

Titration Data	Trial 1
mass of weighing bottle and acid	12.88 g
mass of weighing bottle	12.49 g
mass of solid acid	0.39 g
moles of acid	0.00191 mol
moles of base required	0.00191 mol
final reading of base burette	8.80 mL
initial reading of base burette	1.16 mL
volume of base used in mL	7.64 mL
molarity of base	0.00191 mol

CHEMLAB 19

Analyze and Conclude

1. **Observing and Inferring** Identify the characteristics of this neutralization reaction. **An acid and a base reacted to form a salt and water.**

2. **Collecting and Interpreting Data** Complete the data table. Calculate the number of moles of acid used in each trial by dividing the mass of the sample by the molar mass of the acid. **See data table.**

   $0.39 \text{ g } KHC_8H_4O_4 \times 1 \text{ mol } KHC_8H_4O_4/204.23 \text{ g } KHC_8H_4O_4 = 0.00191 \text{ mol } KHC_8H_4O_4$

3. **Using Numbers** How many moles of base are required to react with the moles of acid you used? **The mole ratio is 1:1, so the number of moles of NaOH is the same as the number of moles of $KHC_8H_4O_4$.**

4. **Using Numbers** Convert the volume of base used from milliliters to liters.
   $7.64 \text{ mL} \times 1 \text{ L}/1000 \text{ mL} = 0.00764 \text{ L}$

5. **Analyze and Conclude** For each trial, calculate the molar concentration of the base by dividing the moles of base by the volume of base in liters.
   $0.00191 \text{ mol}/0.00764 \text{ L} = 0.250M$ **Student results will vary.**

6. **Error Analysis** How well did your calculated molarities agree? Explain any irregularities. **inaccurate burette readings or mass determinations, overshooting the endpoint, spillage, bubbles in the burette**

Real-World Chemistry

1. Use what you have learned about titration to design a field investigation to determine whether your area is affected by acid rain. Research the factors that affect the pH of rain, such as location, prevailing winds, and industries. Form a hypothesis about the pH of rain in your area. What equipment will you need to collect samples? To perform the titration? What indicator will you use? **Student designs should include the selection of a standard solution for titration and the use of Figure 19-18 to choose an indicator. Students may want to form a hypothesis about sources of acid rain and attempt to verify their hypothesis by analyzing samples from various locations. Students could begin their study by collecting samples and testing them with pH paper. Students should outline the steps in a titration of an acid by a strong base similar to the procedure in the ChemLab.**

Name _____ Date _____ Class _____

miniLAB 20

Cleaning by Redox

Applying Concepts The tarnish on silver is silver sulfide, which is formed when the silver reacts with sulfide compounds in the environment. In this miniLAB, you will use an oxidation-reduction reaction to remove the tarnish from silver or a silver-plated object.

Materials aluminum foil, steel wool, small tarnished silver object, 400-mL beaker (or size large enough to hold the tarnished object), baking soda, table salt, hot plate, beaker tongs

Procedure

1. Buff a piece of aluminum foil lightly with steel wool to remove any oxide coating.
2. Wrap the tarnished object in the aluminum foil, making sure that the tarnished area makes firm contact with the foil.
3. Place the wrapped object in the beaker and add sufficient tap water to cover.
4. Add about 1 spoonful of baking soda and about 1 spoonful of table salt.
5. Set the beaker and contents on a hot plate and heat until the water is nearly boiling. Maintain the heat approximately 15 min until the tarnish disappears.

Analysis

1. Write the equation for the reaction of silver with hydrogen sulfide, yielding silver sulfide and hydrogen.

$$2Ag(s) + H_2S(g) \rightarrow Ag_2S(s) + H_2(g)$$

2. Write the equation for the reaction of the tarnish (silver sulfide) with the aluminum foil, yielding aluminum sulfide and silver.

$$3Ag_2S(s) + 2Al(s) \rightarrow 6Ag(s) + Al_2S_3(s)$$

3. Which metal, aluminum or silver, is more reactive? How do you know this from your results? **Aluminum has the greater oxidation potential because it is oxidized in the reaction while silver is reduced.**

4. Why should you not use an aluminum pan to clean silver objects by this method? **The aluminum pan would deteriorate.**

Expected Results: The tarnish is removed from the entire object, not just the part contacting the aluminum.

Name _____ Date _____ Class _____

CHEMLAB 20

Redox Reactions

In Section 20.2, a redox reaction involving copper and nitric acid is discussed. This reaction is balanced by a method called the oxidation-number method. In this lab, you will carry out this reaction, along with another redox reaction that involves a common household substance. You will practice balancing various redox reactions using both the oxidation-number method (from Section 20.2) and the half-reaction method (from Section 20.3).

Problem
What are some examples of redox reactions and how can the equations describing them be balanced?

Objectives
• **Observe** various redox reactions.
• **Balance** redox reactions using the oxidation-number method.
• **Balance** redox reactions using the half-reaction method.

Materials
copper metal
6M nitric acid
evaporating dish
forceps
distilled water
dropper pipette
spoon
household ammonia
crystal drain cleaner
thermometer
250-mL beaker

Safety Precautions
• The reaction of copper with nitric acid should be done in a ventilation hood. Do not breathe the fumes from this reaction.
• Nitric acid and ammonia can cause burns. Avoid contact with skin and eyes.

Pre-Lab
1. Read the entire CHEMLAB.
2. Prepare all written materials that you will take into the laboratory. Be sure to include safety precautions and procedure notes. Use the data table on the next page.
3. Review what a redox reaction is. **A redox reaction is a reaction in which electrons are transferred from one atom to another.**
4. Read the label of the crystal drain cleaner package. Understand that the compound is solid sodium hydroxide that contains aluminum. When the material is added to water, sodium hydroxide dissolves rapidly, producing heat. Aluminum reacts with water in the basic solution to produce $Al(OH)_4^-$ ions and hydrogen gas. Is aluminum oxidized or reduced in the reaction? Is hydrogen oxidized or reduced in the reaction? Explain your answers. **Aluminum is oxidized, due to the loss of three electrons, to form Al^{3+}. Hydrogen is reduced to a zero oxidation number due to the gain of one electron.**

CHEMLAB 20

Procedure

1. In a ventilation hood, place a piece of copper metal in a clean, dry evaporating dish. Add enough 6M nitric acid to cover the metal. **CAUTION:** *Nitric acid can cause burns. The reaction of nitric acid with copper generates dangerous fumes. Use a ventilation hood.* Observe what happens and record your observations in the data table.

2. Pour about 2 mL of the solution from the evaporating dish into a test tube that contains about 2 mL of distilled water. Add ammonia until a change occurs. Record your observation in the data table.

3. Add about 50 mL of tap water to a 250-mL beaker. Use a thermometer to measure the temperature of the water. Record your observations in the data table.

4. Pour approximately 1 cm³ of dry drain cleaner onto a watchglass. **CAUTION:** *Drain cleaner is caustic and will burn skin. Use forceps to move the crystals and observe their composition.* Record your observations in the data table.

5. Carefully pour about one-half spoonful of the crystals into the water in the beaker. As the crystals react with the water, watch the thermometer in the water for a few minutes and record in the data table the highest temperature reached and any other observations you make.

Cleanup and Disposal

1. After step 1 is completed, use forceps to remove any excess pieces of copper metal. Rinse the copper metal with tap water and dispose of the metal as your teacher instructs.

2. After step 2 is finished, pour the solution down the drain and flush with a lot of water.

3. After step 5 is finished, pour the solution down the drain and flush with a lot of water.

Sample Data

Data Table

Step 1	Students should observe bubbles and a blue solution.
Step 2	Students should observe a dark blue solution.
Step 3	The water temperature should be approximately 25°C.
Step 4	Students should observe white and green particles, bits of metal.
Step 5	Students should note the maximum temperature reached—approximately 40°C.

Analyze and Conclude

1. **Applying Concepts** The reaction between copper and nitric acid is discussed in Section 20.2. Write the half-reaction for the substance that is oxidized.
$$Cu \rightarrow Cu^{2+}$$

2. **Applying Concepts** Write the half-reaction for the substance that is reduced.
$$NO_3^- \rightarrow NO_2$$

3. **Thinking Critically** In step 2, a deep blue copper–ammonia complex is formed according to the following reaction.
$$Cu^{2+} + NH_3 \rightarrow Cu(NH_3)_4^{2+}$$
Is this a redox reaction? Why or why not?
It is not a redox reaction because none of the atoms change oxidation number.

CHEMLAB 20

4. **Using Numbers** The following side reaction occurs from the reaction of copper with nitric acid.
$$Cu + HNO_3 \rightarrow Cu(NO_3)_2 + NO + H_2O$$
Balance this redox reaction using both the oxidation-number method and the half-reaction method.
$$3Cu + 8HNO_3 \rightarrow 3Cu(NO_3)_2 + 2NO + 4H_2O$$

5. **Using Numbers** Write and balance the redox reaction of sodium hydroxide with aluminum and water.
$$2NaOH + 6H_2O + 2Al \rightarrow 2Na[Al(OH)_4] + 3H_2$$

6. **Error Analysis** Give possible reasons why you might not have been able to balance the equation for the redox reaction you performed in this experiment.
Answers will vary. Incorrect half-reactions will make it difficult or impossible to balance the redox equation.

Real-World Chemistry

1. Using your observations in this lab, how do drain cleaning crystals remove clogs?
The sodium hydroxide reacts with hair and grease. The reaction gets hot, which helps loosen hair and grease.

2. Ammonia and bleach are two common household chemicals that should never be mixed. One product of this reaction is chloramine, a poisonous, volatile compound. The reaction is as follows.
$$NH_3 + ClO^- \rightarrow NH_2Cl + OH^-$$
What is the balanced redox reaction?
The reaction is balanced as given.

3. One type of Breathalyzer detects whether ethanol is in the breath of a person. Ethanol is oxidized to acetaldehyde by dichromate ions in acidic solution. The dichromate ion in solution is orange, while the Cr^{3+} aqueous ion is green. The appearance of a green color in the Breathalyzer test shows that the breath exceeds the legal limit of alcohol. The equation is
$$H^+ + Cr_2O_7^{2-} + C_2H_5OH \rightarrow Cr^{3+} + C_2H_4O + H_2O$$
Balance this redox reaction.
$$8H^+ + Cr_2O_7^{2-} + 3C_2H_5OH \rightarrow 2Cr^{3+} + 3C_2H_4O + 7H_2O$$

4. Diluted hydrochloric acid can be used to remove limestone (calcium carbonate) surrounding phosphate and silicate fossils. The reaction produces carbon dioxide, water, and aqueous calcium chloride. Write the balanced chemical equation. Is it a redox reaction? Explain.
$$CaCO_3(aq) + 2HCl(aq) \rightarrow CO_2(g) + H_2O(l) + CaCl_2$$
This is not a redox reaction. None of the oxidation numbers change.

Copyright © Glencoe/McGraw-Hill, a division of the McGraw-Hill Companies, Inc.

miniLAB 21
Corrosion

Comparing and Contrasting A lot of money is spent every year correcting and preventing the effects of corrosion. Corrosion is a real-world concern of which everyone needs to be aware.

Materials iron nails (4); magnesium ribbon (2 pieces, each about 5 cm long); copper metal (2 pieces, each about 5 cm long); 150-mL beakers (4); distilled water; saltwater solution; sandpaper

Procedures

1. Use the sandpaper to buff the surfaces of each nail. Wrap two nails with the magnesium ribbon and two nails with the copper. Wrap the metals tightly enough so that the nails do not slip out.

2. Place each of the nails in a separate beaker. Add distilled water to one of the beakers containing a copper-wrapped nail and one of the beakers containing a magnesium-wrapped nail. Add enough distilled water to just cover the wrapped nails. Add salt water to the other two beakers. Record your observations for each of the beakers.

3. Let the beakers stand overnight in the warmest place available. Examine the nails and solutions the next day and record your observations.

Analysis

1. Describe the difference between copper-wrapped nails in the distilled water and salt water after standing overnight.
There is more corrosion of the nail soaking in the saltwater solution than in the distilled water.

2. Describe the difference between the magnesium-wrapped nails in the distilled water and salt water.
There is more corrosion of the magnesium metal in the saltwater solution than in the distilled water.

3. In general, what is the difference between a copper-wrapped nail and a magnesium-wrapped nail?
The nail wrapped in copper corrodes. The nail wrapped in magnesium does not corrode, but the magnesium metal does.

Expected Results: The nails wrapped with copper show corrosion. The copper still looks shiny in each. There is an orange precipitate in each of these beakers. The magnesium is corroded in each of the magnesium-wrapped nails. The nail looks unchanged where the magnesium covered it.

CHEMLAB 21

Voltaic Cell Potentials

A voltaic cell converts chemical energy into electrical energy. It consists of two parts called half-cells. When two different metals, one in each half-cell, are used in the voltaic cell, a potential difference is produced. In this experiment, you will measure the potential difference of various combinations of metals used in voltaic cells and compare these values to the values found in the standard reduction potentials table.

Problem

How can you measure the potential of voltaic cells?

Objectives

- **Construct** voltaic cells using various combinations of metals for electrodes.
- **Design** the arrangement of the voltaic cells in a microplate in such a way as to use materials efficiently.
- **Determine** which metals are the anode and cathode in voltaic cells.
- **Compare** the experimental cell potential to the theoretical value found in Table 21-1.

Materials

metal strips (approximately 0.6 cm by 1.3 cm) of copper, aluminum, zinc, and magnesium
$1M$ copper(II) nitrate
$1M$ aluminum nitrate
$1M$ zinc nitrate
$1M$ magnesium nitrate
24-well microplate
Beral-type pipettes (5)
CBL System
voltage probe
filter paper (6 pieces size 0.6 cm by 2.5 cm)
$1M$ potassium nitrate
forceps
steel wool or sandpaper
table of standard reduction potentials

Safety Precautions

- Always wear goggles and a lab apron.
- The chemicals used in this experiment are eye and skin irritants. Wash thoroughly if they are spilled on the skin.

Pre-Lab

1. Read the entire CHEMLAB.

2. Plan and organize how you will arrange voltaic cells in the 24-well microplate using the four metal combinations so that your time and materials will be used in the most efficient manner possible. Have your instructor approve your plan before you begin the experiment.

3. Prepare all written materials that will take into the laboratory. Be sure to include safety precautions and procedure notes. Use the data table on the next page.

4. Review the definition of a voltaic cell.
A voltaic cell is a device that converts chemical energy to electrical energy.

5. Review the purpose of a salt bridge in the voltaic cell. In this experiment, the filter paper strips soaked in potassium nitrate are the salt bridges.
A salt bridge allows positive and negative ions to travel from one solution to the other.

CHEMLAB 21

6. Review the equation to calculate cell potential.
$E^0_{cell} = E^0_{red} - E^0_{oxid}$

7. For the voltaic cell Mg | Mg²⁺ || Hg²⁺ | Hg, identify which metal is the anode and which metal is the cathode. Which metal is being oxidized and which metal is being reduced? What is the theoretical potential for this voltaic cell?
Mg is anode; Hg is cathode; Mg is oxidized; Hg is reduced; E^0_{cell} = 3.223 V

8. Review the equation to calculate percent error.
[(theoretical potential − actual potential)/theoretical potential] × 100%

Procedure

1. Prepare the CBL to read potential differences (voltage). Plug the voltage probe into Channel 1. Turn the CBL on. Push the MODE button once to activate the voltmeter function.

2. Soak the strips of filter paper in 2 mL of potassium nitrate solution. These are the salt bridges for the experiment. Use forceps to handle the salt bridges.

3. Using the plan from your Pre-Lab, construct voltaic cells using the four metals and 1 mL of each of the solutions. Remember to minimize the use of solutions. Put the metals in the wells that contain the appropriate solution (for example, put the zinc metal in the solution with zinc nitrate). Use a different salt bridge for each voltaic cell. If you get a negative value for potential difference, switch the leads of the probe on the metals.

4. Record which metals are the anode and cathode in each cell in the data table. The black lead of the probe will be attached to the metal that acts as the anode. The red lead will be attached to the cathode.

5. Record the cell potential of each cell.

Cleanup and Disposal

1. Use forceps to remove the metals from the microplate.

2. Rinse the solution off the metal pieces with water, then use steel wool or sandpaper to clean them.

3. Rinse the wells of the microplate.

4. Return each metal to its correct container.

Sample Data

Voltaic Cell Potential Data

	Anode metal (black)	Cathode metal (red)	Actual cell potential (V)	Anode half-reaction and theoretical potential	Cathode half-reaction and theoretical potential	Theoretical cell potential	% Error
1	Al	Cu	+0.703	Al → Al³⁺ + 3e⁻ (+1.662 V)	Cu²⁺ + 2e⁻ → Cu (+0.3419 V)	+2.004 V	64.9%
2	Al	Zn	+0.425	Al → Al³⁺ + 3e⁻ (+1.662 V)	Zn²⁺ + 2e⁻ → Zn (−0.7618 V)	+0.900 V	53.8%
3	Mg	Al	+0.461	Mg → Mg²⁺ + 2e⁻ (+2.372 V)	Al³⁺ + 3e⁻ → Al (−1.662 V)	+0.710 V	35.1%
4	Zn	Cu	+0.942	Zn → Zn²⁺ + 2e⁻ (+0.7618 V)	Cu²⁺ + 2e⁻ → Cu (+0.3419 V)	+1.104 V	14.7%
5	Mg	Cu	+1.65	Mg → Mg²⁺ + 2e⁻ (+2.372 V)	Cu²⁺ + 2e⁻ → Cu (+0.3419 V)	+2.714 V	39.2%
6	Mg	Zn	+1.07	Mg → Mg²⁺ + 2e⁻ (+2.372 V)	Zn²⁺ + 2e⁻ → Zn (−0.7618 V)	+1.610 V	33.5%

CHEMLAB 21

Analyze and Conclude

1. **Applying Concepts** Write the half-reactions for the anode and cathode in each of the voltaic cells in the data table. Look up the half-reaction potentials from the standard reduction potentials table (**Table 21-1**) and record these in the data table. **See data table.**

2. **Using Numbers** Calculate the theoretical potential for each voltaic cell and record it in the data table. **See data table.**

3. **Predicting** Using your data table, rank the metals you used in order of most active to least active.
Al|Al³⁺||Cu²⁺|Cu; Al|Al³⁺||Pb²⁺|Pb; Zn|Zn²⁺||Cu²⁺|Cu; Al|Al³⁺||Zn²⁺|Zn; Zn|Zn²⁺||Pb²⁺|Pb; Pb|Pb²⁺||Cu²⁺|Cu

4. **Using Models** Calculate the percent error of the voltaic cell potential. **See data table.**

5. **Error Analysis** Why is the percent error calculated in step 4 large for some voltaic cells and small for others?
It is hard to get ideal conditions for each cell; therefore, some cells will get better results than others.

Real-World Chemistry

1. Why is lithium metal becoming a popular electrode in modern batteries? Use the standard reduction potentials table to help you answer this question.
Lithium is the highest on the standard reduction potentials chart. If another metal is combined with this in a battery, it will provide a large cell potential. Lithium is also the lightest metal, so it will help reduce the weight.

2. What type of battery is used in pacemakers to regulate a patient's heartbeat? What are some of the benefits of this battery?
Lithium batteries are commonly used in pacemakers because they are lightweight, durable, and long-lasting.

Name _____ Date _____ Class _____

mini LAB 22

Synthesis and Reactivity of Ethyne

Observing and Inferring Ethyne, often called *acetylene*, is used as a fuel in welding torches. In this lab, you will generate ethyne from the reaction of calcium carbide with water.

Materials 150-mL beaker, stirring rod, liquid dishwashing detergent, calcium carbide, forceps, wood splints, matches, ruler about 40 cm long, rubber band, phenolphthalein solution

Procedure

1. Use a rubber band to attach a wood splint to one end of the ruler so that about 10 cm of the splint extends beyond the stick.

2. Place 120 mL water in the beaker and add 5 mL dishwashing detergent. Mix thoroughly.

3. Use forceps to pick up a pea-sized lump of calcium carbide (CaC_2). Do not touch the CaC_2 with your fingers. **CAUTION:** *If CaC_2 dust touches your skin, wash it away immediately with a lot of water.* Place the lump of CaC_2 in the beaker of detergent solution.

4. Use a match to light the splint while holding the ruler at the opposite end. Immediately bring the burning splint to the bubbles that have formed from the reaction in the beaker. Extinguish the splint after observing the reaction.

5. Use the stirring rod to dislodge a few large bubbles of ethyne and determine whether they float upward or sink in air.

6. Rinse the beaker thoroughly, then add 25 mL distilled water and a drop of phenolphthalein solution. Use forceps to place a small piece of CaC_2 in the solution. Observe the results.

Expected Results: When ignited, the ethyne should pop and burn in a yellow-orange ball that rises from the beaker. Soot may be deposited on the sides of the beaker as a result of incomplete combustion. Ethyne, having a molar mass of 26 g/mol, is slightly less dense than air, which has an average molar mass of about 29. Bubbles may float upward slowly but should demonstrate nearly neutral buoyancy. The phenolphthalein should turn pink as $Ca(OH)_2$ is formed.

Analysis

1. Describe your observations in steps 3 and 4. Could ethyne be used as a fuel? **Bubbles form and rise to the surface as the CaC_2 reacts. The bubbles ignite, producing heat, light, and soot. Ethyne is a fuel because it burns.**

2. Based on your observations in step 5, what can you infer about the density of ethyne compared to the density of air? **Density is slightly less than air.**

3. The reaction of calcium carbide with water yields two products. One is ethyne gas (C_2H_2). From your observation in step 6, suggest what the other product is, and write a balanced chemical equation for the reaction. **From the color change, students should realize that a base is produced. Given that the cation present is Ca^{2+}, they may infer that the insoluble material is $Ca(OH)_2$.**

$$CaC_2(s) + 2H_2O(l) \rightarrow C_2H_2(g) + Ca(OH)_2(s)$$

Name _____ Date _____ Class _____

CHEMLAB 22

Analyzing Hydrocarbon Burner Gases

The fuel that makes a Bunsen burner work is a mixture of alkane hydrocarbons. One type of fuel is natural gas, whose primary component is methane (CH_4). The other type is called LP gas and consists primarily of propane (C_3H_8). In this experiment, you will use the ideal gas equation to help identify the main component of your classroom fuel supply.

Problem
What type of alkane gas is used in the burner fuel supplied to your laboratory?

Objectives
• **Measure** a volume of gas by water displacement.
• **Measure** the temperature, pressure, and mass at which the volume of the gas was measured.
• **Calculate** the molar mass of the burner gas using the ideal gas equation.

Materials
barometer
thermometer
1-L or 2-L plastic soft drink bottle with cap
burner tubing
pneumatic trough
100-mL graduated cylinder
balance (0.01g)
paper towels

Safety Precautions
• **Always wear safety goggles and a lab apron.**
• **Be certain that there are no open flames in the lab.**

Pre-Lab
1. Read the entire CHEMLAB.
2. Prepare all written materials that you will take into the laboratory. Include safety precautions and procedure notes. Use the data table on the next page.
3. Use the formulas of methane, ethane, and propane to calculate the compounds' molar masses.
methane (CH_4), **16.04 g/mol;** ethane (C_2H_6), **30.07;** propane (C_3H_8), **44.10**
4. Given R and gas pressure, volume, and temperature, show how you will rearrange the ideal gas equation to solve for moles of gas.
PV = nRT
n = PV/RT
5. Suppose that your burner gas contains a small amount of ethane (C_2H_6). How will the presence of this compound affect your calculated molar mass if the burner gas is predominantly:
   a. methane **The experimental molar mass will be larger.**
   b. propane **The experimental molar mass will be smaller.**
6. Use the data table on the next page.

Expected Results: Natural gas in the U.S. averages about 85% methane, 9% ethane, 3% propane, and 3% composed of nitrogen, butane, and helium.

CHEMLAB 22

Procedure

1. Connect the burner tubing from the gas supply to the inlet of the pneumatic trough. Fill the trough with tap water. Open the gas valve slightly and let a little gas bubble through the tank in order to flush all of the air out of the tubing.

2. Measure the mass of the dry plastic bottle and cap. Record the mass in the data table (bottle + air). Record both the barometric pressure and the air temperature.

3. Fill the bottle to overflowing with tap water and screw on the cap. If some air bubbles remain, tap the bottle gently on the desktop until all air has risen to the top. Take off the cap, add more water, and recap the bottle.

4. Place the thermometer in the trough. Invert the capped bottle into the pneumatic trough and remove the cap while keeping the mouth of the bottle underwater. Hold the mouth of the bottle directly over the inlet opening of the trough.

5. Slowly open the gas valve and bubble gas into the inverted bottle until all of the water has been displaced. Close the gas valve immediately. Record the temperature of the water.

6. While the bottle is still inverted, screw on the cap. Remove the bottle from the water. Thoroughly dry the outside of the bottle.

7. Measure the mass of the bottle containing the burner gas and record the mass in the data table (bottle + burner gas).

8. Place the bottle in a fume hood and remove the cap. Compress the bottle several times to expel most of the gas. Refill the bottle to overflowing with water and determine the volume of the bottle by pouring the water into a graduated cylinder. Record the volume of the bottle.

Cleanup and Disposal

1. Be certain that all gas valves are closed firmly and dump water out of pneumatic troughs.

2. Clean up water spills and dispose of materials as directed by your teacher.

3. Return all lab equipment to its proper place.

Sample Data

Mass and Volume Data	
Mass of bottle + air (g)	30.49 g
Mass of air (g)	0.82 g
Mass of "empty" bottle (g)	29.67 g
Mass of bottle + collected burner gas (g)	30.30 g
Mass of collected burner gas (g)	0.63 g
Barometric pressure (atm)	1.01 atm
Temperature (°C)	24°C
Temperature (K)	297 K
Volume of gas collected (L)	0.630 L

Analyze and Conclude

1. **Acquiring Information** Use the volume of the bottle and look up the density of air to compute the mass of the air the bottle contains. Use gas laws to compute the density of air at the temperature and pressure of your laboratory. The density of air at 1 atm and 20°C is 1.205 g/L.

    mass of air = density × volume   See sample data table.

2. **Using Numbers** Calculate the mass of the empty bottle by subtracting the mass of air from the mass of the bottle and air combined. **See sample data table.**

3. **Using Numbers** Determine the mass of the collected gas by subtracting the mass of the empty bottle from the mass of the bottle and gas. **See sample data table.**

CHEMLAB 22

4. **Interpreting Data** Use the volume of gas, water temperature, and barometric pressure along with the ideal gas law to calculate the number of moles of gas collected.

    At 25°C, approximately 3% of the volume of the bottle will be occupied by water vapor because the gas was collected over water. However, the molar mass of water is near that of methane, the component most likely to be present in the gas supply. Therefore, the presence of water vapor may be ignored in an experiment of this precision. Students substitute values into the ideal gas equation and solve for *n*. Before they calculate, consider having students estimate the value of *n* based on the known volume of the bottle and Avogadro's principle.

5. **Using Numbers** Use the mass of gas and the number of moles to calculate the molar mass of the gas.

    Students should carry out the following calculation.

    molar mass = measured mass of gas/calculated number of moles

6. **Drawing a Conclusion** How does your experimental molar mass compare with the molar masses of methane, ethane, and propane? Suggest which of these gases are in the burner gas in your laboratory.

    Results will depend on the composition of the gas.

7. **Error Analysis** If your experimental molar mass does not agree with that of any one of the three possible gases, suggest possible sources of error in the experiment. What factor other than error could produce such a result?

    Possibilities include excess water trapped in the bottle, incorrect or poor measurement techniques, or math error. A gas mixture would yield a molar mass that does not exactly equal the molar mass of any of the components.

Real-World Chemistry

1. Substances called *odorants* are mixed with natural gas before it is distributed to homes, businesses, and institutions. Why must an odorant be used, and what substances are used as odorants?

    Odorants are added to warn people of the presence of gas. They are typically H_2S and mercaptans (thiols and thioethers), such as ethyl mercaptan, methyl mercaptan, dimethyl sulfide, and methylethyl sulfide.

2. At 1 atm and 20°C, the densities of methane and propane are 0.65 g/L and 1.83 g/L, respectively. Would either gas tend to settle in a low area such as the basement of a home? Explain.

    Yes. Propane would because it is more dense than air.

CHEMLAB 23

Properties of Alcohols

Alcohols are organic compounds that contain the —OH functional group. In this experiment, you will determine the strength of intermolecular forces of alcohols by determining how fast various alcohols evaporate. The evaporation of a liquid is an endothermic process, absorbing energy from the surroundings. This means that the temperature will decrease as evaporation occurs.

Problem

How do intermolecular forces differ in three alcohols?

Objectives

- **Measure** the rate of evaporation for water and several alcohols.
- **Infer** the relative strength of intermolecular forces of alcohols from rate of evaporation data.

Materials

thermometer
stopwatch
facial tissue
cloth towel
Beral pipettes (5)
methanol
ethanol (95%)
2-propanol (99%)
wire twist tie or small rubber band
piece of cardboard for use as a fan

Safety Precautions

- Always wear safety goggles and a lab apron.
- The alcohols are flammable. Keep them away from open flames.

Pre-Lab

1. Read the entire CHEMLAB.

2. Prepare all written materials that you will take into the laboratory. Be sure to include safety precautions and procedure notes. Use the data table on the next page.

3. Draw structural formulas for the three alcohols you will use in this activity. Describe how the structures of these compounds are alike and how they are different. CH_3OH, CH_3CH_2OH, and $CH_3CH(OH)CH_3$. **All structures contain the hydroxyl group. Parent chains are different, and the hydroxyl group is on the middle carbon in 2-propanol.**

4. What types of forces exist between these kinds of molecules? Suggest which alcohol may have the greatest intermolecular forces. **hydrogen bonding; 2-propanol likely has the greatest intermolecular forces.**

Procedure

1. Cut out five 2-cm by 6-cm strips of tissue.

2. Place a thermometer on a folded towel lying on a flat table so that the bulb of the thermometer extends over the edge of the table. Make sure the thermometer cannot roll off the table.

3. Wrap a strip of tissue around the bulb of the thermometer. Secure the tissue with a wire twist tie placed above the bulb of the thermometer.

4. Choose one person to control the stopwatch and read the temperature on the thermometer. A second person will put a small amount of the liquid to be tested into a Beral pipette.

5. When both people are ready, squeeze enough liquid onto the tissue to completely saturate it. At the same time, the other person starts the stopwatch, reads the temperature, and records it in the data table.

6. Fan the tissue-covered thermometer bulb with a piece of cardboard or other stiff paper. After one minute, read and record the final temperature in the data table. Remove the tissue and wipe the bulb dry.

---

miniLAB 23

Making an Ester

Observing and Inferring Flowers and fruits have pleasant odors partly because they contain substances called esters. Companies make blends of synthetic esters to mimic the flavors and fragrances of esters found in nature. In this experiment, you will make an ester that has a familiar smell.

Materials salicylic acid, methanol, distilled water, 10-mL graduated cylinder, Beral pipette, 250-mL beaker, concentrated sulfuric acid, top or bottom of a petri dish, cotton ball, small test tube, balance, weighing paper, hot plate, test-tube holder

Procedure

1. Prepare a hot-water bath by pouring 150 mL of tap water into a 250-mL beaker. Place the beaker on a hot plate set at medium.

2. Place 1.5 g of salicylic acid in a small test tube and add 3 mL of distilled water. Then add 3 mL of methanol and 3 drops of concentrated sulfuric acid to the test tube. **CAUTION:** *Sulfuric acid is corrosive. Handle with care.*

3. When the water is hot but not boiling, place the test tube in the bath for 5 minutes.

4. Place the cotton ball in the petri dish half. Pour the contents of the test tube onto the cotton ball. Record your observation of the odor of the product.

Analysis

1. The ester you produced has the common name oil of wintergreen. Write a chemical equation using names and structural formulas for the reaction that produced the ester.

salicylic acid + methanol → methyl salicylate + water. The structure of methyl salicylate is similar to the esters shown on page 751. The structure of salicylic acid is shown on page 752.

2. What are the advantages and disadvantages of using synthetic esters in consumer products as compared to using natural esters? **Student answers may vary. Advantage: synthetic esters are more efficiently and economically produced than natural esters. Disadvantage: odors of synthetic esters may differ slightly from those of natural esters, which may contain other compounds.**

3. Name some products that you think could contain the ester you made in this experiment. **Student answers will vary but may include chewing gum and mint candy.**

Expected Results: The product will have a wintergreen odor.

CHEMLAB 23

7. Repeat steps 3 through 6 for each of the three alcohols: methanol, ethanol, and 2-propanol. If your teacher has another alcohol, use it also.

Cleanup and Disposal

1. Place tissues in the trash. Pipettes can be reused.

Analyze and Conclude

Sample Data

Evaporation Data

Substance	Starting temp (°C)	Temp after 1 minute (°C)	ΔT (°C)
Water	21	19	2
Methanol	22	8	14
Ethanol	22	13	9
2-Propanol	21	16	5
Other alcohol			

1. **Communicating** Formulate a statement that summarizes your data, relating temperature change to the substances tested. Do not draw any conclusions yet.

In order of decreasing temperature change, the liquids are methanol, ethanol, 2-propanol, and water.

2. **Acquiring and Analyzing Information** Explain why the temperatures changed during the experiment.

Because evaporation is endothermic, heat is transferred from the tissue paper to the liquid as it evaporates.

3. **Observing and Inferring** What can you conclude about the relationship between heat transfer and the differences in the temperature changes you observed?

The greater the heat transfer during evaporation, the greater the temperature change.

4. **Drawing Conclusions** Assume that the three alcohols have approximately the same molar enthalpy of vaporization. What can you say about the relative rates of evaporation of the three alcohols?

Methanol may have the highest relative rate of evaporation, then ethanol, then 2-propanol.

5. **Drawing Conclusions** Consider your answer to question 4. What can you conclude about the relative strength of intermolecular forces existing in the three alcohols?

Intermolecular forces of attraction between molecules appear to increase as the length of the carbon chain in the alcohol gets longer.

6. **Predicting** Suppose you also tested the alcohol 1-pentanol in this experiment. Where among the alcohols tested would you predict 1-pentanol to rank in rate of evaporation from fastest to slowest? Describe the temperature change you would expect to observe. Explain your reasoning.

1-pentanol would likely rank between 2-propanol and water in the list. ΔT would probably be 3°C or 4°C. As the longest-chain alcohol, 1-pentanol should evaporate more slowly than 2-propanol but faster than water.

CHEMLAB 23

7. **Thinking Critically** Molar enthalpies of vaporization for the three alcohols are given in the table on the right. Note that they are not the same. In what way, if any, does this data change your conclusion about intermolecular forces?

The data reinforce the conclusion that intermolecular forces increase as the length of the carbon chain in the alcohol increases. The heat of vaporization is a measure of the strength of these forces. The data also support the conclusion in Question #4.

Molar Enthalpies of Vaporization

Substance	Enthalpy of vaporization at 25°C (kJ/mol)
Methanol	37.4
Ethanol	42.3
2-Propanol	45.4

8. **Observing and Inferring** Make a general statement comparing the molecular size of an alcohol in terms of the number of carbons in the carbon chain to the rate of evaporation of that alcohol.

The rate of evaporation appears to decrease as the number of carbon atoms increases.

9. **Error Analysis** Suggest a way to make this experiment more quantitative and controlled.

Care could be taken to make sure the pieces of tissue are the same size, air movement is equal, and exactly the same amount of each alcohol is used.

Real-World Chemistry

1. How can this experiment help explain why small-chain alcohols have a warning label indicating that they are flammable?

Because small-chain alcohols evaporate quickly, they produce much vapor. Alcohol in the vapor phase is very reactive, and therefore very flammable.

2. Would you expect to see such a warning label on a bottle of 1-decanol? Explain.

No. Because it is a long-chain alcohol, 1-decanol likely has a low volatility.

3. A mixture of 70% 2-propanol (isopropanol) and 30% water is sold as rubbing alcohol, which may be used to help reduce a fever. Explain how this process works.

Both compounds have relatively high enthalpies of vaporization. Therefore, the skin of a feverish person must lose an appreciable amount of heat to the liquids as they evaporate, cooling the skin.

4. Why do you suppose that 2-propanol is a component in some products used to soothe sunburned skin?

The endothermic evaporation of 2-propanol helps cool the sunburned skin.

miniLAB 24
A Saponification Reaction

Applying Concepts The reaction between a triglyceride and a strong base such as sodium hydroxide is called saponification. In this reaction, the ester bonds in the triglyceride are hydrolyzed by the base. The sodium salts of the fatty acids, called soaps, precipitate out, and glycerol is left in solution.

Materials solid vegetable shortening, 250-mL beaker, 600-mL beaker, 6.0M NaOH, ethanol, saturated NaCl solution, stirring rod, hot plate, tongs, 25-mL graduated cylinder, evaporating dish, cheesecloth (20 cm × 20 cm), funnel

Procedure

1. Place a 250-mL beaker on the hot plate. Add 25 g solid vegetable shortening to the beaker. Turn the hot plate on at a medium setting.
2. As the vegetable shortening melts, slowly add 12 mL ethanol and then 5 mL 6.0M NaOH to the beaker. **CAUTION:** *Ethanol is flammable. NaOH causes skin burns. Wear gloves.*
3. Heat the mixture, stirring occasionally, for about 15 minutes, but do not allow it to boil.
4. When the mixture begins to thicken, use tongs to remove the beaker from the heat. Allow the beaker to cool for 5 minutes, then place it in a cold-water bath in the 600-mL beaker.
5. Add 25 mL saturated NaCl solution to the mixture in the beaker. The soap is not very soluble and will appear as small clumps.
6. Collect the solid soap clumps by filtering them through a cheesecloth-lined funnel.
7. Using gloved hands, press the soap into an evaporating dish. Allow the soap to air dry for 1 or 2 days.
8. Remove your gloves and wash your hands. **Expected Results: The small bar of soap can be molded into an evaporating dish.**

Analysis

1. What type of bonds present in the triglycerides are broken during the saponification reaction?
ester bonds

2. What is the common name for the sodium salt of a fatty acid?
a soap

3. How does soap remove dirt from a surface?
One end of the soap molecule is a nonpolar hydrocarbon that attracts the soil. The other end of the soap molecule contains the sodium ion and is ionic. This end is attracted to polar water molecules. The dirt-laden soap is flushed away with the water.

4. Write a word equation for the saponification reaction in this lab.
triglyceride plus sodium hydroxide yields glycerol plus soap

CHEMLAB 24

Alcoholic Fermentation in Yeast

Yeast cells are able to metabolize many types of sugars. In this experiment, you will observe the fermentation of sugar by baker's yeast. When yeast cells are mixed with a sucrose solution, they must first hydrolyze the sucrose to glucose and fructose. Then the glucose is broken down in the absence of oxygen to form ethanol and carbon dioxide. You can test for the production of carbon dioxide by using a CBL pressure sensor to measure an increase in pressure.

Problem

What is the rate of alcoholic fermentation of sugar by baker's yeast?

Objectives

- **Measure** the pressure of carbon dioxide produced by the alcoholic fermentation of sugar by yeast.
- **Calculate** the rate of production of carbon dioxide by the alcoholic fermentation of sugar by yeast.

Materials

CBL system
graphing calculator
ChemBio program
Vernier pressure
  sensor
link cable
CBL-DIN cable
test tube with #5
  rubber-stopper
  assembly
5% sucrose solution

ring stand
stirring rod
600-mL beaker
thermometer
basting bulb
hot and cold water
yeast suspension
vegetable oil
utility clamp
10-mL graduated
  cylinders (2)
pipette

Safety Precautions

- Always wear safety goggles and a lab apron.
- Do not use the thermometer as a stirring rod.

Pre-Lab

1. Reread the section of this chapter that describes alcoholic fermentation.
2. Write the chemical equation for the alcoholic fermentation of glucose.
$$C_6H_{12}O_6 \rightarrow 2CH_3CH_2OH + 2CO_2 + energy$$
3. Read the entire CHEMLAB.
4. Prepare all written materials that you will take into the laboratory. Be sure to include safety precautions and procedure notes.
5. Form a hypothesis about how the pressure inside the test tube is related to the production of carbon dioxide during the reaction. Refer to the ideal gas law in your explanation.
Rearranging the ideal gas law to solve for pressure, $P = (nRT)/V$. Therefore, as carbon dioxide is produced, n increases, which increases P.

Expected Results: Pressure will increase in the tube as carbon dioxide gas is produced.

CHEMLAB 24

6. Why is temperature control an essential feature of the CHEMLAB?

The ideal gas law clearly shows that P is dependent on T. Therefore, if T changes during the experiment, the change in pressure will be the combined result of carbon dioxide production and temperature change.

Procedure

1. Load the ChemBio program into your graphing calculator. Connect the CBL and calculator with the link cable. Connect the pressure sensor to the CBL with a CBL-DIN cable.

2. Prepare a water bath using the 600-mL beaker. The beaker should be about two-thirds full of water. The water temperature should be between 36°C and 38°C.

3. Set up the test tube, ring stand, and utility clamp. Obtain about 3 mL yeast suspension in a 10-mL graduated cylinder, and pour it into the test tube. Obtain about 3 mL 5% sucrose solution in a 10-mL graduated cylinder. Add the sucrose solution to the yeast in the test tube. Stir to mix. Pour enough vegetable oil on top of the mixture to completely cover the surface.

4. Place the stopper assembly into the test tube. Make sure it has an airtight fit. Leave both valves of the assembly open to the atmosphere.

5. While one lab partner does step 5, the other partner should do steps 6 and 7. Lower the test tube into the water bath and allow it to incubate for 10 minutes. Keep the temperature of the water bath between 36°C and 38°C by adding small amounts of hot or cold water with the basting bulb as needed.

6. Start the ChemBio program. Choose 1:SET UP PROBES under MAIN MENU. Choose 1 for number of probes. Choose 3:PRESSURE under SELECT PROBE. Enter 1 for Channel. Choose 1:USE STORED for CALIBRATION. Choose 1:ATM for PRESSURE UNITS.

7. Choose 2:COLLECT DATA under MAIN MENU. Choose 2:TIME GRAPH under DATA COLLECTION. Use time between sample seconds = 10. Use number of samples = 60. (This will give you 600 seconds or 10 minutes of data). Choose 1:USE TIME SETUP under CONTINUE? Set Ymin = 0.8, Ymax = 1.3, and Yscl = 0.1. Do not press ENTER until the test tube has finished incubating.

8. After the test tube has incubated for 10 minutes, close the valve attached to the stopper. Make sure the valve near the pressure sensor is open to the sensor. Start measuring the gas pressure by pressing ENTER. Monitor the pressure reading on the CBL unit. If the pressure exceeds 1.3 atm, the stopper can pop off. Open the air valve on the pressure sensor to release this excess gas pressure.

9. After 10 minutes, the data collection will stop. Open the air valve on the stopper. If needed, you can run a second trial by closing the air valve and choosing 2:YES to REPEAT? If you are finished, press 1:NO.

Cleanup and Disposal

1. Rinse out and wash all items.

2. Rinse the yeast suspension/sucrose/vegetable oil mixture down the sink with large amounts of water.

3. Return all lab equipment to its proper place.

CHEMLAB 24

Analyze and Conclude

1. **Making and Using Graphs** Choose 3:VIEW GRAPH from the MAIN MENU. Make a sketch of the graph. (You also may want to record the data table by using 4:VIEW DATA.)

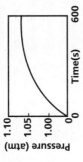

Pressure (atm) vs. Time(s); y-axis: 1.10, 1.05, 1.00; x-axis: 0 … 600

2. **Interpreting Data** The rate of carbon dioxide production by the yeast can be found by calculating the slope of the graph. Return to the MAIN MENU and choose 5:FIT CURVE. Choose 1:LINEAR L1, L2. The slope will be listed under LINEAR as "A" of $Y = A*X + B$. Record this value.

Answers will vary. The typical slope will be 0.00024 atm/s.

3. **Communicating** How does your rate of carbon dioxide production compare with the rates of other members of the class?

Answers will vary. Results should be fairly close.

4. **Analyzing** Why did you add vegetable oil to the test tube in step 3?

The vegetable oil sealed the reaction mixture from the air, ensuring that fermentation and not cellular respiration took place in the tube.

5. **Error Analysis** Suppose that the pressure does not change during a trial. What might be some possible reasons for this?

Pressure would not change if there was a small leak in the apparatus. Also, if the vegetable oil does not cover the surface of the reaction mixture, oxygen will be used up as fast as carbon dioxide is produced as the yeast undergoes cellular respiration.

Real-World Chemistry

1. Yeast is used in baking bread because the carbon dioxide bubbles make the bread rise. The other product of alcoholic fermentation is ethanol. Why can't you taste this alcohol when you eat bread?

The ethanol evaporates as the bread is baked.

2. How would the appearance of a loaf of bread be different if you used twice as much yeast as the recipe called for?

The loaf of bread would be higher and fluffier if twice the amount of yeast was used.

Name _____ Date _____ Class _____

miniLAB 25

Modeling Radioactive Decay

Formulating Models Because of safety concerns, it is usually not possible to directly experiment with radioactive isotopes in the classroom. Thus, in this lab, you will use pennies to model the half-life of a typical radioactive isotope. Each penny represents an individual atom of the radioisotope.

Materials 100 pennies, 5-oz or larger plastic cup, graph paper, graphing calculator (optional)

Procedure

1. Place the pennies in the plastic cup.

2. Place your hand over the top of the cup and shake the cup several times.

3. Pour the pennies onto a table. Remove all the pennies that are "heads-up." These pennies represent atoms of the radioisotope that have undergone radioactive decay.

4. Count the number of pennies that remain ("tails-up" pennies) and record this number in the Decay Results data table as the Number of pennies remaining for trial 1.

5. Place all of the "tails-up" pennies back in the plastic cup.

6. Repeat steps 2 through 5 for as many times as needed until no pennies remain.

Expected Results: The Decay Results table should show that approximately half of the pennies decay during each trial. There will probably be no pennies remaining after 7 to 9 trials.

Decay Results

Trial number	Number of pennies remaining
0	100
1	
2	
3	
4	
5	
6	
7	
8	

Analysis

1. Make a graph of Trial number versus Number of pennies remaining from the Decay Results data table. Draw a smooth curve through the plotted points. **The graph should show an exponential decay, and in general should resemble the shape of the curve seen in Figure 25-13.**

2. How many trials did it take for 50% of the sample to decay? 75%? 90%? **It took approximately one trial for 50% of the sample to decay. It took approximately two trials for 75% of the sample to decay. It took approximately four trials for 90% of the sample to decay.**

3. If the time between each trial is 1 minute, what is the half-life of the radioisotope? **The half-life is 1 minute.**

4. Suppose that instead of using pennies to model the radioisotope, you use 100 dice. After each toss, any die that comes up a "6" represents a decayed atom and is removed. How would the result using the dice compare with the result obtained from using the pennies? **Approximately one-sixth of the dice will decay with each toss. It would take approximately three tosses to get one-half of the sample to decay.**

Name _____ Date _____ Class _____

CHEMLAB 25

Measuring Naturally Occurring Radiation

As you may know, some common everyday substances are radioactive. In this lab, you will investigate the three naturally occurring potassium isotopes found in a common store-bought salt substitute. Two of potassium's isotopes, potassium-39 (93.1%) and potassium-41 (6.89%) are stable. However, potassium-40 (0.01%) decays by beta emission to form stable calcium-40. You will first measure the background radiation level, and then use that information to determine the radiation due to the beta decay of potassium-40. You will also measure radiation at various locations around your school.

Problem

How can you determine if a substance contains radioactive isotopes?

Objectives

• **Measure** background radiation and radiation emitted by a radioactive isotope.

• **Compare** the level of background radiation to the level of radiation emitted by a radioactive isotope.

Materials

CBL system
RADIATIN software program
graphing calculator
link-to-link cable
Student Radiation Monitor
CBL-P adapter
TI GRAPH LINK
petri dish (with lid)
salt substitute or pure potassium chloride (KCl)
balance

Safety Precautions

• Always wear safety goggles and a lab apron.

Pre-Lab

1. Read the entire CHEMLAB.

2. Prepare all written materials that you will take into the laboratory. Include any necessary safety precautions and procedure notes. Use the data table on the next page.

3. What is an isotope? A radioactive isotope? **Isotopes are atoms of the same element that have the same atomic number but different atomic masses due to having different numbers of neutrons. A radioactive isotope, also known as a radioisotope, is an unstable isotope that will undergo radioactive decay.**

4. Write the nuclear equation for the radioactive decay of potassium-40 by beta emission. Identify the "parent" and "daughter" nuclides in the decay.

$$^{40}_{19}K \rightarrow ^{40}_{20}Ca + ^{0}_{-1}\beta$$

parent → daughter + $^{0}_{1}\beta$

CHEMLAB 25

5. Using nuclide-stability rules, form a hypothesis that explains why calcium-40 should be a more stable nuclide than potassium-40.
Potassium-40 has an n/p ratio of 21 : 19, or 1.105 : 1. Calcium-40 has an n/p ratio of 20 : 20, or 1 : 1. Calcium-40's lower n/p ratio makes it more stable.

Procedure

1. Load the program RADIATIN into the graphing calculator.
2. Connect the graphing calculator to the CBL system using the link-to-link cable. Connect the CBL system to the Student Radiation Monitor using the CBL-P adapter. Turn on all devices. Set the Student Radiation Monitor on the audio setting and place it on top of an empty petri dish.
3. Start the RADIATIN program. Go to MAIN MENU. Select 4:SET NO. SAMPLE. Choose 20 for the number of samples in each reading. Press ENTER.
4. Select 1:COLLECT DATA from the MAIN MENU. Select 4:TRIGGER/PROMPT from the COLLECTING MODE menu. Press ENTER to begin collecting data. After a few seconds, the calculator will ask you to enter a PROMPT. Enter 1 (because this is the first data point) and press ENTER. Choose 1:MORE DATA under TRIGGER/PROMPT.
5. Press ENTER to begin the next data point. A graph will appear. When asked to enter the next PROMPT, enter the number that appears at the top right corner of the calculator screen, and then press ENTER. Choose 1:MORE DATA under TRIGGER/PROMPT.
6. Repeat step 5 until you have at least five data points. This set of data is the background level of radiation from natural sources.

7. Use the balance to measure out 10.0 g salt substitute or pure potassium chloride (KCl). Pour the substance into the center of the petri dish so that it forms a small mound. Place the Student Radiation Monitor on top of the petri dish so that the Geiger Tube is positioned over the mound. Repeat step 5 until you have at least five data points.
8. When you are finished collecting data, choose 2:STOP AND GRAPH under TRIGGER/PROMPT. The data points (PROMPTED) are stored in L1, the counts per minute (CTS/MIN) are stored in L2. Press ENTER to view a graph of data.

Cleanup and Disposal

1. Return the salt substitute or potassium chloride (KCl) used in the experiment to the container prepared by your instructor.
2. Disconnect the lab setup and return all equipment to its proper place.

Radiation Level Data

Data point	Counts/min
1	21.9
2	17.5
3	17.4
4	19.2
5	19.2
6	43.3
7	76.5
8	79.3
9	93.3
10	67.0
11	65.0
12	54.6

For this sample data, points 1–5 were background radiation levels and points 6–12 were KCl radiation levels.

CHEMLAB 25

Analyze and Conclude

1. **Collecting Data** Record the data found in L1 and L2 (STAT, EDIT) in the Radiation Level Data table. **See data table.**
2. **Graphing Data** Graph the data from L1 and L2. Use the graph from the graphing calculator as a guide. **Check that student graphs accurately portray their data.**
3. **Interpreting Data** What is the average background radiation level in counts/minute? **The average for background radiation (data points 1–5) is 19.0 counts/min.**
4. **Interpreting Data** What is the average radiation level in counts/minute for the potassium-40 isotope found in the salt substitute? **The average for KCl radiation level (data points 6–12) is 68.4 counts/min.**
5. **Observing and Inferring** How can you explain the difference between the background radiation level and the radiation level of the salt substitute? **Since the KCl has radiation levels higher than background radiation levels, it must contain an isotope undergoing radioactive decay.**
6. **Thinking Critically** Is the data for the background radiation and the radiation from the potassium-containing sample consistent or random in nature? Propose an explanation for the pattern or lack of pattern seen in the data. **A pattern of randomness may appear when collecting data for radiation levels for both background radiation and potassium-40. Radiation decay is a chance event, so levels measured over a short period of time are more likely to be random. If measured over a sufficient period of time, the data will take on a bell-shaped curve.**
7. **Error Analysis** Describe several ways to improve the experimental procedure so it yields more accurate radiation level data. **Accuracy of measuring a radiation level can be improved by collecting data over a longer period of time.**

Name _____ Date _____ Class _____

CHEMLAB 25

Real-World Chemistry

1. Arrange with your teacher to plan and perform a field investigation using the experimental setup from this experiment to measure the background level radiation at various points around school or around town. Propose an explanation for your findings.

Findings and explanations will vary. Higher radiation levels may be found near

industrial sites that use radioisotopes in the manufacture of products.

2. Using the procedure in this lab, determine if other consumer products contain radioisotopes. Report on your findings.

Results will vary depending upon the consumer product tested.

Name _____ Date _____ Class _____

miniLAB 26

Acid Rain in a Bag

Making a Model Acid precipitation often falls to Earth hundreds of kilometers away from where the pollutant gases enter the atmosphere because the gases diffuse through the air and are carried by the wind. In this lab, you will model the formation of acid rain to observe how the damage caused by acid varies with the distance from the source of pollution. You also will observe another factor that affects the amount of damage caused by acid rain.

Materials plastic petri dish bottom; 1-gallon zipper-close, plastic bag; white paper; droppers; 0.04% bromocresol green indicator; 0.5M KNO_2; 1.0M H_2SO_4; clock or watch

Procedure

1. Place 25 drops of 0.04% bromocresol green indicator of varying sizes in the bottom half of a plastic petri dish so that they are about 1 cm apart. Be sure that there are both large and small drops at any given distance from the center. Leave the center of the petri dish empty.

2. Place a zipper-close, plastic bag on a piece of white paper.

3. Carefully slide the petri dish containing the drops of indicator inside the plastic bag.

4. In the center of the petri dish, place 1 large drop of 0.5M KNO_2. To this KNO_2 drop, add 2 drops of 1.0M H_2SO_4. **CAUTION:** KNO_2 and H_2SO_4 are skin irritants. Carefully seal the bag. Observe whether the mixing of these two chemicals produces any bubbles of gas. This is the pollution source.

5. Observe and compare the color changes that take place in the drops of indicator of different sizes and distances from the pollution source. Record your observations every 15 seconds.

6. To clean up, carefully remove the petri dish from the bag, rinse it with water, then dry it.

Analysis

1. As the gas reacts with water in the drops, two acids form, $2NO_2 + H_2O \rightarrow HNO_3 + HNO_2$. What are these acids? HNO_3—nitric acid, HNO_2—nitrous acid

2. Did the small or large drops change color first? Why? **The small drops changed color first. The surface area-to-volume ratio is greater.**

3. Did the distance of the indicator drops from the pollution source have an effect on how quickly the reaction occurred? Explain. **The drops that were closer to the pollution source reacted faster because diffusion of the pollution occurred over a shorter distance.**

4. State two hypotheses that will explain your observations, and incorporate the answers from questions 2 and 3 in your hypotheses. **The gas diffuses and dissolves faster in water drops that are smaller and closer to the source.**

---

miniLAB

Acid Rain in a Bag, *continued*

5. Based on your hypotheses in question 4, what can you infer about the damage done to plants by acid fog as compared with acid rain? **Acid fog would do more damage to plants than acid rain in the same area because the surface area-to-volume ratio is greater.**

Expected Results: Bubbles of NO_2 gas appear in the colorless center drop. The blue drops change to yellow as the NO_2 gas dissolves in the drops. The smaller drops completely change color first. The larger drops change color on the outer surface first. The drops farthest from the source change last.

ChemLab and MiniLab Worksheets

CHEMLAB 26

Solar Pond

If you made a list of popular types of alternative energy sources, solar energy probably would be near the top. Of course, the energy we use from all sources ultimately originates from the Sun. It would seem that solar energy would be the easiest to use. The problem is how to store solar energy when the Sun is not shining. In this experiment, you will investigate one method that could be used to trap and store solar energy.

Expected Results: Students will find that the saturated salt-solution layer retains the heat better than the tap-water layer.

Problem

Build a small-scale model of a solar pond and test how it traps and stores solar energy.

Objectives

- **Construct** a small-scale solar pond using simple materials.
- **Collect** temperature data as the solar pond model heats and cools.
- **Hypothesize** as to why a solar pond is able to trap and store solar energy.

Materials

CBL System
graphing calculator
ChemBio program
link-to-link cable
temperature probes (2)
150-watt lightbulb
socket and clamp for bulb
black plastic frozen-dinner dish
waterproof tape
table salt
hot plate
stirring rod
250-mL beaker
beaker tongs
TI GRAPH LINK (optional)
ring stand and clamp
250-mL graduated cylinder

Safety Precautions

- **The lightbulb will become hot when it is turned on.**
- **Do not touch the hot plate while it is on.**

Pre-Lab

1. Read the entire CHEMLAB.
2. Prepare all written materials that you will take into the laboratory. Include safety precautions and procedure notes.
3. Water is transparent to visible light but opaque to infrared radiation. How do you think these properties will affect your solar pond model? **Heat will not penetrate the water in the upper layer, but light energy will reach the bottom.**
4. If you used only tap water in your model, convection currents would bring warmer, less dense water from the bottom to the surface. Do you think this will happen with your solar pond model? Explain your answer. **No; the warm salt water will not rise to the surface because it is denser than the tap water.**

ChemLab and MiniLab Worksheets

ChemLab and MiniLab Worksheets Answer Key

Name _____ Date _____ Class _____

CHEMLAB 26

5. Predict which of the two layers of the model will have the higher final temperature. Explain your prediction.

The salt-water layer will have the higher final temperature because there are no convection currents to bring the warm water to the surface to be cooled.

Procedure

1. Prepare a saturated table salt (NaCl) solution by heating 100 mL of tap water in a beaker on a hot plate. When the water is boiling, slowly add enough table salt to saturate the solution while stirring with a stirring rod. Remove the beaker from the hot plate with beaker tongs and allow the solution to cool slowly overnight.

2. The next day, prepare the solar pond model. Place the black plastic dish on the lab bench where you want to run the experiment. Use a small piece of waterproof tape to attach one of the temperature probes to the bottom of the black plastic dish. Plug this probe into Channel 1 of the CBL System. Slowly pour the 100 mL of saturated salt solution into the dish.

3. Carefully add about 100 mL of tap water on top of the saturated salt-water layer in the dish. Use care not to mix the two layers. Suspend the end

of the second temperature probe in the tap-water layer and plug it into Channel 2 of the CBL System.

4. Connect the graphing calculator to the CBL System using the link cable. Turn on both units. Run the ChemBio program. Choose 1:SET UP PROBES under MAIN MENU. Choose 2 probes. Under SELECT PROBE, choose 1:TEMPERA-TURE. Enter 1 for Channel. This is for the probe at the bottom of the salt-water layer. Under SELECT PROBE, choose 1: TEMPERATURE. Enter 2 for Channel. This is for the probe in the tap-water layer.

5. Under MAIN MENU, choose 2: COLLECT DATA. Choose 2: TIME GRAPH. For time between samples in seconds, choose 30. For number of samples, choose 60. This will allow the experiment to run for 30 minutes. Set the calculator to use this time setup. Input the following: $Ymin = 0$, $Ymax = 30$, $Yscl = 1$. Do not start collecting data yet.

6. Position the 150-watt lightbulb about 15 to 20 cm over the top of the solar pond model. Turn on the light. Press ENTER on the calculator to begin collecting data. After about 6 to 8 minutes, turn off the lightbulb and move it away from the solar pond model. Do not disturb the experiment until the calculator is finished with its 30-minute run.

Cleanup and Disposal

Rinse the salt solution off the temperature probes.

Analyze and Conclude

1. **Graphing Data** Make a copy of the graph from the graphing calculator. If you have TI GRAPH LINK and a computer, do a screen print.

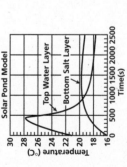

Solar Pond Model — Temperature (°C) vs Time(s); Top Water Layer, Bottom Salt Layer

---

Name _____ Date _____ Class _____

CHEMLAB 26

2. **Interpreting Graphs** Describe the shape of each curve in the graph of time versus temperature before and after the lightbulb was turned off. Explain the significance of the difference.

Water layer—the curve climbs rapidly until the bulb is turned off, when it falls rapidly. Salt layer—curve climbs steadily. When the bulb is turned off, the curve levels off. This indicates that heat is retained.

3. **Comparing and Contrasting** Which layer of your solar pond model did the best job of trapping and storing heat?

The salt-water layer traps and stores heat better.

4. **Applying Concepts** Why does the graph of time versus temperature decrease more rapidly near the surface when the lightbulb is turned off?

Contact with the cooler air causes rapid cooling. Evaporation of the warm water causes the water to lose heat.

5. **Forming a Hypothesis** Make a hypothesis to explain what is happening in your model.

Convection currents do not occur because salt water is denser than tap water. Thus, the warm salt water does not rise to the surface to be cooled.

6. **Designing an Experiment** How would you test your hypothesis?

Repeat the experiment using colored salt water. The color will not mix with the water layer if there is no convection.

7. **Error Analysis** How might your results have been different if you had used a white dish instead of a black dish? Explain.

The bottom layer will not warm up as rapidly because the white dish will not absorb as much heat as the black dish.

Real-World Chemistry

1. Water in a lake rises to the surface when heated and sinks to the bottom when cooled in a process called convection. Compare and contrast the density of the water as it rises with the density of the water as it sinks.

The density of the water decreases as it rises and increases as it sinks.

2. The El Paso Solar Pond was the first in the world to successfully use solar pond technology to store and supply heat for industrial processes. It was built with three main layers: a top layer that contains little salt, a middle layer with a salt content that increases with depth, and a very salty bottom layer that stores the heat. Which layer has the greatest density? The least density? Why doesn't the storage layer in the El Paso Solar Pond cool by convection?

The density of the layers decreases from bottom to top. The storage layer doesn't cool by convection because its density is greater than that of the layers above it.